S0-ABC-160

THIS CHANGING
EARTH

ABOUT THE AUTHOR

John A. Shimer was born in Boston, Massachusetts, in 1913, and graduated from Derby Academy in Hingham, Massachusetts. He received his B.S. degree from Harvard in 1935; his M.S. from M.I.T. in 1939; and his Ph.D. from M.I.T. in 1942. From 1946 to the present, he has been Professor of Geology at Brooklyn College. Dr. Shimer is the author of *This Sculptured Earth: The Landscape of America* (1959) and co-author of *Graphic Methods in Structural Geology* (1958).

EVERYDAY HANDBOOKS

THIS CHANGING
EARTH

AN INTRODUCTION TO GEOLOGY

BY JOHN A. SHIMER

Drawings by Genevieve Shimer

BARNES & NOBLE, Inc. NEW YORK
Publishers Booksellers Since 1873

This Changing Earth: An Introduction to Geology

Published by Barnes & Noble, Inc.
through special arrangement with Harper & Row, Publishers, Inc.

Copyright © 1968 by John A. Shimer

All rights reserved. No part of this book may be used or reproduced in any manner whatsoever without written permission except in the case of brief quotations embodied in critical articles and reviews. For information address Harper & Row, Publishers, Incorporated, 49 East 33rd Street, New York, N.Y. 10016.

Reprinted, 1969

L.C. Catalog Card Number: 71-85880

Printed in the United States of America

TO GENNY

CONTENTS

CONTENTS

DRAWINGS AND DIAGRAMS

X   DRAWINGS AND DIAGRAMS

PHOTOGRAPHS

PREFACE

This book attempts to give some idea of what geology is about and some of the problems which are currently tantalizing the earth scientist. The topics selected for discussion emphasize the ever-changing physical aspect of the earth, as well as how ideas concerning the earth have constantly changed in response to new information.

Historically, geology has been largely an observational science, where the noting of field relationships has led more or less directly to conclusions concerning fundamental geologic relationships and processes. Laboratory work consisted in large measure of drafting maps and sections, and analyzing and classifying minerals, rocks, and fossils. Recently in the study of the earth the techniques and approaches of physics and chemistry have been applied to a greater and greater extent, and now a large variety of quite sophisticated detecting and measuring devices have become standard tools of the earth scientist.

The geologist today, in marked contrast with those of a generation ago, knows much more about the earth. Artificial satellites have made possible the determination of the shape and gravity field of the earth in much greater detail than ever before. Present-day maps of the sea floor show a great deal of detail, and the amount and distribution of heat flow from the earth is known. The three-dimensional distribution of rock types and densities in the crust and upper mantle has been determined, in broad outline at least, from seismic evidence. Furthermore, the refinement of various types of high-pressure and temperature devices has enabled the geologist to reproduce probable upper mantle conditions in the laboratory, and in this fashion check ideas concerning the composition and mineralogy of materials there.

The development of the knowledge of natural radioactivity and the greatly increased precision in measuring isotope abundances in the last few decades have resulted in modern quantitative geochronology. This, in turn, has had a profound effect in all branches of geology. The paleontologist has now a quantitative yardstick against which to measure rates of evolution, the stratigrapher has a better idea of the rates of sedimentation, and the structural geologist can begin to build up a quantitative table for rates and times of deformation of the crust.

Some of the still most mysterious and least clear aspects of the earth for the geologist are those which involve the major relief features, the continents and ocean basins, and the zonal arrangement of the earth into crust, mantle, and core. The whole complex structure of the earth and the origin of its many parts is now challenging the geologist as never before. The ultimate goal, of course, is to integrate all the observations concerning the physical, chemical, and biological nature of the world into a coherent whole, and explain them as the outcome of a rational history. Such a goal will probably never be completely possible of attainment. However, as more information is obtained and more basic questions are asked and finally answered, the picture of the earth and the life on it as a dynamic interrelated evolving system will become ever clearer.

THIS CHANGING
EARTH

The Grand Tetons, Wyoming. A fault-block mountain range, carved by water and ice.

(Union Pacific Railroad)

CHAPTER I

INTRODUCTION

Ever since the earth came into being over 4½ billion years ago, its surface has been changing. Evidence of crustal instability is undeniable. However stable the earth's surface may appear to be in one place, in another it is in motion. It moves as a hot liquid, shifts up or down or sideways as a solid in blocks and masses or, as small particles, it is blown, washed, or slides down slopes. Throughout geologic history this continued unrest has turned inland seas into mountains, and these in turn into lowlands. An interpretation of the record left in the rocks enables us to recreate in the mind former aspects of the earth's surface. Present rocks and landscapes betray their former experiences to the discerning eye.

The varieties of crustal unrest can conveniently be divided into three major groups under the geological processes of gradation, igneous activity, and diastrophism. Gradation includes weathering (the process of rock breakup) and erosion (the removal and eventual dumping elsewhere of that debris). The agents of erosion are running water, wind, underground water, ocean waves and currents, and glaciers, all aided by the ever present force of gravity which pulls loose fragments down any available slope. Igneous activity includes the extrusion of lava flows and volcanoes, and the intrusion of liquid rock into the crust. Diastrophism includes faulting, folding, uplifting, and downwarping—that is, in general any movement of the solid parts of the earth with respect to each

1

other. In diastrophism crustal material is moved en masse, not piecemeal as in gradation, or as a hot liquid during igneous activity.

The major landforms, such as mountains, plateaus, and in fact any part of the crust uplifted above sea level, result from the constructive processes of diastrophism and igneous activity. It is gradation that destroys these uplifted regions, and in so doing produces the finer scenic details which so diversify the land, the cliffs, rapids, waterfalls, hill slopes, and the almost infinite variety of rock shapes and surfaces.

Until quite recently, the explanation of natural wonders in the world around us was based on the concept of creation which implied that the earth's surface was formed all at once a few thousand years ago. Mountains, valleys, plains were manifestations of the glory of God; they could be enjoyed but their origin could not be understood. It was not until the middle of the nineteenth century that scientists generally accepted the fact that the earth has been in existence for a very long time, and that the present landscape can be explained as the result of forces and events similar to those currently operating, working slowly throughout long stretches of time, measured in many thousands if not millions of years. This concept of uniform change, now given the formidable title Principle of Uniformitarianism, was discussed by James Hutton in a series of lectures which he delivered before the Royal Society of Edinburgh in 1785. It explains the available facts in a simple manner, and involves very few assumptions. Later, in 1795, Hutton published his ideas in *The Theory of the Earth with Proofs and Illustrations*. Fortunately, since his writing was obscure and hard to read, his ideas were given new impetus and were popularized by John Playfair, who published *Illustrations of the Huttonian Theory of the Earth* in 1802. Later, in 1833, Charles Lyell published the third and last volume of what was to become a classic textbook, incorporating and amplifying the ideas of Hutton and Playfair. This book went through many revisions during the middle of the nineteenth century, and was very important in the education of generations of geologists.

Prior to the acceptance of the Principle of Uniformitarianism the concept of Catastrophism explained landscape features as having been created quite dramatically almost overnight. The catastrophist called on major happenings far in excess of the work of any recorded tidal wave, flood, earthquake, or volcanic eruption to explain major landscape features, such as mountain ranges or deep canyons. The modern geologist will agree that the several geologic processes have undoubtedly varied greatly in the rate at which they have changed the land during earth history. He will not, however, accept rates much in excess of those historically verified. For instance, the production of such a feature as the Grand Canyon in northern Arizona, or a major sea-cliff hundreds of feet high, or a mountain range such as the Sierra Nevada Mountains in California, towering thousands of feet in the air, is now believed to have required the cumulative effect of many relatively small geologic events spread out through thousands and perhaps millions of years. The Grand Canyon appears essentially the same year after year, no matter how much debris the river removes, or how much crumbles and slides down the canyon walls. Time is needed for the presently noted changes cumulatively to give us the canyon. With time, however, the Colorado River can easily be visualized as having carried away all the material now missing between the north and south rims of the canyon, by slowly, year in year out, washing away material which falls down the canyon walls to it, and using this debris as abrasive material to cut ever deeper into the rocks of its bed. Similarly, the fashioning of the Sierra Nevada Mountains consisted of the cumulative results of many actions. A long series of spasmodic uplifts, a few feet at a time along the eastern margin fault, accompanied by the shaping of the peaks by weather, ice, and running water, are the essential actions here. In order that the mountains should have the elevation that they do, the uplift must obviously have been at a faster rate than the wearing down.

Each of the major earth processes, igneous activity, gradation, diastrophism, is associated with one of the three major groups of rocks. Igneous rocks are formed from the cooling and consequent solidification of melted hot material. Such material when it appears on the earth's surface is lava, and under the surface it is called magma. Lava generally cools quickly into a glassy to fine-grained rock. If gas is dissolved in the emerging liquid it will expand on reaching the earth's surface and a frothy (vesicular) type of volcanic rock will result, such as the light-colored pumice or the dark-colored scoria, the differences in color being due to differences in chemical composition. Associated with pumice and having the same composition are the light-colored fine-grained rocks such as rhyolite and andesite, and the black glass, obsidian. Dark, fine-grained basalt has the same chemical composition as scoria, only lacking the large quantity of dissolved gases when it was extruded at the surface. Instead of issuing out at the earth's surface to form lava, magma may cool at depth; it will do so slowly and the resulting intrusive igneous rock will be much coarser grained than the extrusive lava rocks. The very widespread light-colored granite and the extremely coarse-grained granite pegmatite have the same chemical composition as their extrusive cousins rhyolite, pumice, and obsidian. And similarly a basaltic magma if cooled at depth will form the coarse-grained dark-colored rock gabbro. It is thus seen that each igneous-rock name implies both a definite chemical composition and a type of texture, which indicates the environment of cooling.

Sedimentary rocks are formed when various types of loose debris produced at the earth's surface are buried, and in this new environment are changed into solid rock. The consolidation of mud, sand, or gravel produces shale, sandstone, and conglomerate, respectively. The accumulation and later burial of organic debris forms coal, and a sediment composed primarily of calcium carbonate in the form of shells or lime mud yields limestone.

Metamorphic rocks, associated with diastrophism, result when heat, pressure, or percolating hot solutions modify pre-existing sedimentary or igneous rocks. Slate is formed from shale by recrystallization of the shale minerals under directed pressure, quartzite is the metamorphic equivalent of sandstone, and marble a recrystallized metamorphic form of limestone. Schist and gneiss are two foliated (layered) types of metamorphic rock, schist being finely foliated and gneiss more coarsely foliated or banded. They likewise are produced under conditions of heat and pressure from some previous rock, which may have been igneous, sedimentary, or even metamorphic. Often the antecedents of these rocks are unknown.

Earth materials are constantly adjusting to changing environments. Any solid rock at the surface of the earth is unstable as such and breaks up, often with changes of mineralogy, to form mud, sand, and gravel. Such sediments in turn are unstable when buried and are consolidated into sedimentary rock by compaction and cementation. Under conditions of still higher temperatures and pressures, sedimentary rocks will be transformed into metamorphic, which in turn under higher temperatures yet may be melted to eventually cool into an igneous rock. This rock cycle represents a constant adjustment of earth materials to changes in environment as they are moved from place to place.

The present appearance of any rock is the result of its past history and in the case of some metamorphic rocks it may be possible to trace a very complex history indeed, if enough evidence is left. Most commonly, however, late changes are all too apt to obscure the record so that it may be wholly indecipherable. For instance, once a rock has been melted and then cooled essentially all evidence of its previous history has been erased cleanly away. However, the relative abundances of various types of atoms and isotopes may give at times some clue concerning past history. Metamorphic changes of all gradations can be found, from those which barely alter the parent rock to those which so alter it that the initial type can only be guessed at.

The major earth processes were active very early in earth history. For instance, rocks over 3 billion years old have been identified as sedimentary in origin. This obviously means that over 3 billion years ago still earlier rocks were broken into small fragments by weathering and then rain washed them downslope to ancestral oceans. Furthermore, forces of diastrophism and igneous activity must have been present so that land areas could be elevated.

There is no fossil evidence that any plant or animal found a home on the land 3 billion years ago, and the presence of life in the sea in the very early days is problematical. Up to about 300 million years ago the landscape must in certain respects have resembled a modern desert, a place where rain, to be sure, fell, but absolutely no plants grew, and no animal wandered across the surface. We must picture the land as utterly barren with no soil and no vegetation to smooth and soften the transition from cliff to slope to valley floor. As a consequence, erosion was probably very rapid; just as fast as rocks were weathered, material was washed down slopes and thence carried by rivers into the sea.

To anyone who has studied the evidence left in the rocks, it is obvious that landscapes of the past have evolved into those of the present by the simple passage of time and the interplay of wind, water, and ice working under varying climatic controls on different types of rocks and rock structures. Modern landscapes are geologically very new in that their carving and shaping is recent, in fact all are being modified before our eyes. Their present shape and rate of change may be controlled, however, by geological events of long ago. For example, the Ridge and Valley area of the Appalachian Mountains is composed of folded sedimentary rocks which were deposited as sediments in a sea many millions of years ago, and crumpled more recently, but still millions of years ago. Weathering and erosion followed, and now ridges and cliffs are present where the more resistant sandstone and conglomerate layers outcrop, and where the weaker shales and limestones are present, the modern landscape shows valleys and gentle slopes. Thus the location and spacing of the hills and valleys in this area are dependent on the location and spacing of the various sedimentary layers as they were crumpled into folds.

Nature is forever striving for final equilibrium. If a part of the land is higher it is torn down. Now after 4½ billion years of earth history the earth seems to be as far from equilibrium as it ever was. This of course means that there must be a tremendous and continuing supply of energy which has constantly caused the disarrangement of earth materials.

The source and application of the energy from within the earth needed to melt the crust and push up mountain ranges is not too clearly known, but undoubtedly the breakdown of radioactive elements with the accompanying production of enormous quantities of heat plays a very important part in this phase of crustal instability.

The energy needed for the process of gradation is supplied by the sun. The winds of the world result from the solar heating of the atmosphere, varying from place to place. Furthermore, the sun has supplied the energy needed to evaporate and raise water from the sea, so that it could fall on the land, and from there flow back to the oceans. Such solar energy has been available ever since the solar system was formed and has been applied in its present manner to earth materials ever since there was an atmosphere and the first rain fell and washed the first rock fragments off the land.

(National Park Service)

The Grand Canyon of the Colorado from the South Rim

CHAPTER II

THE MEASUREMENT OF
GEOLOGIC TIME

Once we accept the general Principle of Uniformitarianism it becomes obvious that the earth is very old measured in terms of a human life span. If the various features of the earth are the result of present-day geologic processes working at more or less the present-day rate, rather than the result of cataclysmic events of the recent past, the length of geologic time must clearly be measured in many thousands if not millions of years. An idea of the truly great length of time that the earth has been in existence has been formed only recently in the twentieth century by the use of methods based on radioactivity. Prior to this, relative ages could be given to geologic materials and events by the recognition and interpretation of certain relationships between rock units, and the lengths of some comparatively short time intervals could be calculated from the measurement of the magnitude of a geologic result divided by the rate at which it was produced.

Relative methods of geologic dating rest on the recognition of three basic relationships now dignified as geologic laws. In a sequence of sedimentary rocks the youngest layer, composed of the most recently deposited material, is at the top, and the layers become progressively older as we dig deeper and deeper into a sequence. This is the Law of Superposition, and is simply a commonsense recognition that the existence of a foundation must precede the deposition of anything found thereon. Second, an igneous intrusion is obviously younger than the rock which it intrudes. This relationship, the Law of Intrusion, recognizes the relative ages between intrusions and the rocks which they intersect, whatever kind of rock they may be, sedimentary, metamorphic, or older igneous rock itself. A third law, that of Faunal and Floral Succession, established by William Smith just before 1800, is based on the recognition that fossil faunas and floras succeed one another in a definite order through geologic time. Working primarily in southern England, especially in connection with the surveying and cutting of the early canals there, Smith discovered that groups of different kinds of fossils found in the rock layers succeeded one another in the same definite sequence wherever they might be found. In places certain fossils might be absent, that is, the layers in which they should have occurred were missing, but each layer that was present was always found to be in its proper sequence as determined by its contained fossils. A fossil, which is any evidence of past life found in a rock, can thus be used as an index to give the relative age of a sedimentary rock unit, once the sequence of fossil forms has been determined. This law of course presupposes an acceptance of the Law of Superposition.

It is now recognized that the changing of plants and animals throughout geologic time is the direct result of the evolution of living forms. The keynote of the inorganic world, instability and change, is equally true in the organic world. Present plants and animals are descendants of past forms in an unbroken succession of relationship. Members of a succession most distant in time differ most from each other. Thus, the farther down we go into the strata of the earth, that is, the older and older sedimentary layers we investigate, the more unlike the present forms do the fossil forms become. It has apparently been true that each species of life, just like an individual, has a shorter or longer life span, after which it disappears forever from the earth's surface. Once a specific type of fossil form representing a specific type of life has disappeared from the rock record, an exactly similar form has never been found in succeeding younger layers.

Age determinations, which give some idea of the long time intervals which must be appreciated when dealing with geological events and processes, are based on the recognition of some geologic result and the rate at which it must have been accomplished. For instance, there is a thinly bedded shale found in a number of places in Wyoming, Utah, and Colorado which contains freshwater fossils, notably very well-preserved fish remains, and represents sediments laid down in a number of isolated lake basins, whose former presence is now indicated only by these deposits. This Green River shale is characteristically composed of alternating light- and dark-colored laminae, which most geologists believe represent seasonal changes in sedimentation. Each pair represents one year's deposit and, by counting up the number of paired laminae in one foot and multiplying by the total thickness, it has been calculated that the lakes were in existence for 8 to 10 million years. Throughout this time, about 50 million years ago, they fluctuated greatly in size as is indicated by the interfingering of the banded lake deposits with river-formed delta and floodplain material.

Geophysical prospecting has shown that the present Mississippi River delta is a surface deposit resting on a total sequence of sediments over 40,000 feet thick. Such a tremendous mass must have taken many millions of years to accumulate by the yearly addition of material washed from the land, if one is to assume that the present annual contribution of the Mississippi River is indicative of past conditions.

Around 1900 John Joly determined the age of the oceans as about 100 million years. He argued that if the seas started as fresh water early in earth history, and if all of the salt present in them now was brought down by the rivers, their age could be calculated by dividing the total salt content by the yearly addition. Obviously, a number of assumptions were made in addition to that of sea water being initially fresh. It was assumed that the rate of salt addition was uniform and that no salt was extracted from the sea throughout this same time interval. The last assumption can be shown to be subject to large errors. Layers of salt interbedded in a number of sedimentary sequences in many areas of the world show that at various times throughout earth history bodies of sea water have been cut off from the main ocean areas and evaporated.

Furthermore, it is believed that at present there is probably more land above sea level and at a higher elevation than during most of geologic time and, because of this, salt is being added to the seas at a greater rate than at most times in the past. Thus although it is difficult to estimate how much, the age of the oceans as calculated by Joly is too young.

Somewhat earlier Lord Kelvin calculated the age of the earth by assuming that it had cooled from a liquid to the present solid, and figured that it would have taken between 20 and 40 million years for this to happen. Reasonable assumptions were made as to the rates at which the initially liquid and the later solid earth would radiate heat.

For truly quantitative age determinations and the measurement in years of the actual antiquity of a specific rock or geologic event, we must turn to the methods based on radioactivity. Obviously, when radioactivity was discovered at the end of the nineteenth century the method used by Lord Kelvin to calculate the age of the earth was immediately recognized as invalid, inasmuch as the radioactive breakdown of elements supplies a great deal of heat energy. Radioactive age determinations in addition to giving accurate quantitative ages can of course be used to give relative ages for unfossiliferous rocks. For instance, fossils are so scarce in rocks 600 million years old—Precambrian in age—that they cannot be used as a means of correlation. Actually for over 90 per cent of geologic time there are no other methods than those based on radioactivity for determining even relative ages, except in localized areas, where the laws of Intrusion and Superposition can be applied. It is fortunate that in both igneous and metamorphic rocks it is easy to date with radioactive methods, since they generally possess the proper minerals.

The history of radioactive methods of dating starts in 1896 when Henri Becquerel discovered natural radioactivity. In 1906 Ernest Rutherford suggested that lead was produced from uranium or thorium by natural disintegration, and in 1907 Bertram Boltwood published a list of geologic dates based on the uranium-lead method. He showed that the ratio of lead to uranium had a characteristic value for uranium minerals in any given locality, and he suggested that this ratio changed with the age of the mineral, that is, that the ratio of lead to uranium increased with time. Many of his dates are now found to be inaccurate, but at least he did demonstrate that geologic time had to be measured in millions of years.

Radioactivity occurs when the composition of the nucleus of an atom spontaneously changes. For instance, in the breakdown of the nucleus of a uranium atom, helium atoms (alpha particles), electrons (beta particles), and much radiant energy (gamma rays) are emitted before the process stops with eventual appearance of a lead atom. Incidentally, if the mass of the end product, lead, plus all the particles which are produced in the various stages of the disintegration are added together, it is found that the total is somewhat less than the original mass of the uranium. It is this loss of mass which has been converted into energy according to Einstein's well-known equation $E = mc^2$, where E is the energy which appears on the loss of the mass m, and c is the velocity of light.

The nucleus of any atom contains two different types of particles, protons and neutrons. Neutrons are electrically neutral, but protons have a positive charge, which is balanced in a neutral atom by the negative charge of an equal number of electrons surrounding the nucleus. The difference between the atom of one element and another lies in the number of protons possessed by the nucleus. Hydrogen, for instance, is the lightest element and has a single proton in its nucleus, whereas uranium, the heaviest naturally occurring element, has 92 protons. All atoms with the same number of protons are chemically alike. The number of neutrons, however, may vary and give alternate forms of an element or isotopes. Isotopes of a given element are thus chemically alike but differ in atomic weight. Some isotopes are unchanging; some are radioactive, with the composition of the nuclei changing spontaneously. Radioactive decay in the natural state proceeds at a constant rate independent of external conditions, such as temperature, pressure, or the chemical environment of the minerals and rocks in which the radioactive elements are found.

With the discovery of isotopes and ways of separating one from another by means of an instrument called a mass spectrograph, refinements came so that radioactive age determinations were far more accurate than in the earlier days of Boltwood.

The general principles of radioactive age determinations are simple. The process of decay starts essentially with a pile of radioactive parent atoms, such as uranium, which on the passage of time transform themselves into another pile of daughter atoms, lead. The longer the time, the larger the pile of lead atoms and the smaller the pile of parent uranium atoms. The rate of this change is often given in terms of the half-life of the radioactive element, or the time that it takes for one-half of an original supply of parent atoms to disappear. For instance, the half-life of one of the varieties of uranium, uranium-235, is 4.5×10^9 years. Radioactive decay has the strange attribute that the elapse of another 4.5×10^9 years will not see the total transformation of the remaining uranium atoms, but of only $\frac{1}{2}$ of them. And after three half-lives $\frac{1}{8}$ of the original mass will remain, and so on. It is impossible to predict when a specific atom will disintegrate, but when large numbers are considered, statistics can be applied and half-life has a definite meaning.

There are a number of conditions which must be fulfilled if radioactive ages are to be correct. All determinations assume a constancy of rate for the breakdown. A further condition necessitates that the host mineral containing the radioactive isotope must neither have gained nor lost any of either the radiogenic daughter or the original radioactive element. That is, the assumption is made that we are dealing with a closed system, the composition of which has been slowly changing only by radioactive change, not by addition or subtraction of material to or from the outside. Also, in most methods it is assumed that there is no radiogenic daughter element present at the start of the breakdown process. This is generally a valid assumption, since a crystal structure which admits the presence of a radioactive element is not such as will accept initially a different-sized daughter element with different chemical characteristics. Daughter elements found in a crystal have been caught and exist in it as small amounts of impurities between the other elements.

A radioactive date may be ambiguous because it may represent any one of a number of ages. We may have obtained the time since the last and only crystallization of the rock, the time since the last of several times of metamorphism, the age of the parent rock from which a new rock was made, such as the age of a conglomerate pebble incorporated into a new sedimentary rock, or lastly, some intermediate age between the extremes mentioned.

There are a number of parent-daughter pairs that are used and if concordant ages by these different systems are obtained, the presumption seems to be valid that the conditions which we have set up as necessary have essentially been met.

The following table gives some commonly used parent-daughter pairs, and their half-lives.

Parent	Daughter	Half-Life (Years)
Uranium^{238}(U^{238})	Lead^{206}(Pb^{206})	4.5x10^9
Uranium^{235}(U^{235})	Lead^{207}(Pb^{207})	7.1x10^8
Thorium^{232}(Th^{232})	Lead^{208}(Pb^{208})	1.5x10^{10}
Rubidium^{87}(Rb^{87})	Strontium^{87}(Sr^{87})	5.0x10^{10}
Potassium^{40}(K^{40})	Argon^{40}(A^{40})	1.3x10^9
Carbon^{14}(C^{14})	Nitrogen^{14}(N^{14})	5730

Note that the superscripts refer to the atomic mass numbers of the isotopes, that is, the number of protons plus neutrons in the nucleus. For instance, all uranium atoms possess 92 protons in the nucleus; thus the number of neutrons in each different isotope of uranium can be determined by subtracting 92 from the mass number.

Because of their very long half-lives, and slow production of daughter products, the U/Pb, Th/Pb, and Rb/Sr methods can only be applied, with any degree of accuracy, to rocks at least a million years old. Enough daughter atoms must have been produced to be measurable. Refinements in laboratory techniques have enabled the K/A method to be applied to rocks as young as 50,000 years old.

A cross-check of uranium-lead ages can be made if both U^{235} and U^{238} are present. The decay rates of these two isotopes are different and thus the ratio of their daughters, Pb^{207}/Pb^{206} will change with time and will give an age which can be checked against the U^{235}/Pb^{207} and U^{238}/Pb^{206} ages.

The carbon-14 method of age determination was developed by W. F. Libby in 1947, and can be used for relatively short lengths of time, up to about 70,000 years ago. Beyond this time there is not enough radioactive carbon left to be measurable. This method has been found very useful in dating archeological material such as any kind of artifact made of wood, plant fibers or shells.

The radioactive isotope of carbon, C^{14}, is produced in the upper atmosphere from nitrogen by the action of cosmic rays. Carbon-14 after being formed will combine with oxygen to give carbon dioxide, which, mixed with the rest of the atmosphere, will eventually be incorporated to a small but measurable extent in the parts of any living organism. As soon as any plant or animal dies and is buried the percentage of C^{14} present will decrease at a rate given by the half-life, as no more can of course be incorporated. Thus the amount of radioactive carbon left is a measure of how long the given material has been cut off from a supply of carbon-14; the smaller the amount, the longer the length of burial, that is, the longer an object has been sitting away from carbon-14 replenishment. Note that in this method instead of measuring the concentration of a daughter and comparing it with the amount of parent left, the ratio of parent only, the carbon-14, to ordinary carbon-12 is measured, because the assumption is made that the carbon-14 concentration at the time of burial is known.

The percentage of radioactive carbon to ordinary carbon at any one time is very small, but if there is good distribution in the air and oceans, which absorb much of the carbon dioxide of the earth, the assumption can be made that any growing organism is exposed to a supply of carbon with a definite but small amount of the carbon-14 isotope, mixed in with the far more common isotope, carbon-12. The amount of carbon-14 present at any one time is of course dependent on the rate of production and the rate of decay. The rate of decay has been demonstrated to be constant and the production rate has been assumed to have been essentially constant throughout the last few thousand years. However, recently it has been shown that there are slight variations in the C^{14} content of eighteenth- and nineteenth-century wood correlated with sunspot activity. A slightly higher percentage of C^{14} than expected is associated with greater solar activity which has resulted in the production of a more than average amount of C^{14} in the upper atmosphere of the earth. Incidentally, the recent use of atomic energy and the testing of bombs has increased the abundance of carbon-14 to some extent. This will not affect the ages of organic material now buried, but will certainly affect the atmospheric and oceanic abundance.

The first test of the accuracy of radiocarbon dating was made by comparing known historical dates of material, such as early Roman and Egyptian artifacts, with their radiocarbon dates. They were found to agree very well up to at least 5,000 years before the present.

An example of one of the hazards which besets radioactive age determinations concerns some interesting "fictitious" carbon-14 dates which have been reported in certain rather special cases. For instance, if modern shells grow in an environment where they get carbon from humus which has been buried for a long time or from dissolving limestone, they will have less carbon-14 than shells growing in an environment which is constantly replenished with the radioactive form from the upper atmosphere.

Minerals differ markedly in their ability to hang onto radiogenic daughter elements during a period of metamorphism, and this may lead to discordant ages for different minerals in the same rock. An example of such discordant ages has been found in the Baltimore gneiss. The age of the zircon crystals in this rock, using the uranium-lead method is 1,100 million years, the Rb/Sr method also gives 1,100 million years to the feldspars in the rock, but the biotite ages are 300 million years as given by both Rb/Sr and the K/A methods. The biotite of a granite intruded into this older gneiss also has an age of 300 million years, and a feldspar age of 350 to 400 million years. Thus it appears that the biotite age of the Baltimore gneiss represents a time of metamorphism connected with the intrusion of the granite. The biotites have apparently lost their daughter products at the time of intrusion, whereas the zircons and feldspars have held onto theirs.

Another example of discordant ages has been worked out in a Colorado granite 54 million years old which has intruded a Precambrian rock 1,300 million years old. Dates on various minerals in the Precambrian rocks right next to the younger intrusive all agree with the younger date of the intrusion. However, as samples are dated in the Precambrian rocks farther and farther away from the intrusion the dates as determined by the various methods approach the Precambrian age.

The radioactive methods using isotopes are by far the most commonly used and the most highly developed of modern age determination techniques. Other types of procedure have been investigated and have proved to be useful in certain situations. For example, radiation from radioactive impurities in certain minerals can cause damage to the host mineral, and comparison of the extent of the damage with the intensity of the radiation gives a basis for time calculations. The use of pleochroic halos in biotites is an example of this method. These discolored rings surrounding an inclusion containing some radioactive element have been produced by radiation from the inclusion, and the width and intensity of discoloration have been found to be a measure of the time. Here, one must assume that all samples of biotite react the same to the same intensity and duration of radiation.

The age of the earth as somewhat over 4.5 billion years has been determined in an indirect fashion from the age of meteorites. The assumption is made that the meteorites as well as the planets were formed at approximately the same time, and that if meteorites show an age of 4.5 billion years the chances are fairly good that the earth itself is approximately that old. Rb-Sr, K-A, and U-Pb measurements on stony meteorites all give ages of the order of magnitude of 4.5 billion years. Again the necessary assumptions here are that the meteorites have existed as isolated closed systems, that is, that no parent radioactive elements or daughter products have been added or subtracted throughout their lives.

It seems to be relatively easy to find rocks between 2,500 and 2,700 million years old on most continents. It is much rarer, however, to find rocks over 3,000 million years old. The oldest rocks found to date in Africa lie between 3 and 3.3 billion years; in Europe there are rocks which have been dated 3.5 billion years; in North America 3.1 to 3.5 and in Australia slightly over 3 billion. Thus, the question arises, where are the rocks between 3.5 and 4.5 billion years old, since none has yet been found in this age range. Their lack may be due to the complete metamorphism of any rocks over 3.5 billion years old, or the explanation may lie in the absence of any continental material at that early time in earth history.

Present continental materials vary in antiquity from place to place. Age determination of many rocks in North America has shown that there appears to be a rough zoning in the continent. The oldest, those over 3 billion years, are found in a belt extending from the Hudson Bay area southwestward to the northern Rockies, with younger rocks either side. Such an arrangement can be explained in one of two ways. Either the continent has grown by the accretion of rocks around a central core, or the zoning is the result of the reworking of older material during more recent times of metamorphism. There is no general agreement as to which of these two alternatives is nearer the truth.

It is now clear that the earth is very much older than was suspected before radioactive age determinations were made, and that the Precambrian, that is, the time before fossils can be used for relative dating, includes as much as $\frac{9}{10}$ of all of geologic time. However, the recognition that rocks differed in relative ages was appreciated early in the history of geology. Giovanni Arduino, 1714-1795, was one of the first to attempt the subdivision of the geologic record into definite time intervals. He was professor of mineralogy and metallurgy in Venice, and was also in the government mining service. By 1759 he had recognized divisions of rock ages to be noted in the southern Alps and on the northern Italian plains. His basis of classification was purely lithological. The cores of the mountains were composed of crystalline rocks, igneous or metamorphic in origin. These he called Primary. The flanks of the mountains were composed of steeply tilted and folded sedimentary rocks, with fossils. These he called Secondary. Farther away from the mountains, lying on top of the secondary rocks in places, were low mounds and hills of gravel and sand and marl, with here and there some volcanic material. These were obviously younger than the two previous groups and were named Tertiary. The more modern term, "Quaternary," was added in 1830 for recent river and lake deposits currently accumulating.

The present geologic time chart was developed in the nineteenth century. The terms "Tertiary" and "Quaternary" are still used as holdovers from the earlier system of names. The modern chart with its era, period, and epoch names is based on information of relative ages determined from fossils. This chart is arranged with the oldest divisions at the bottom, emphasizing the fact that

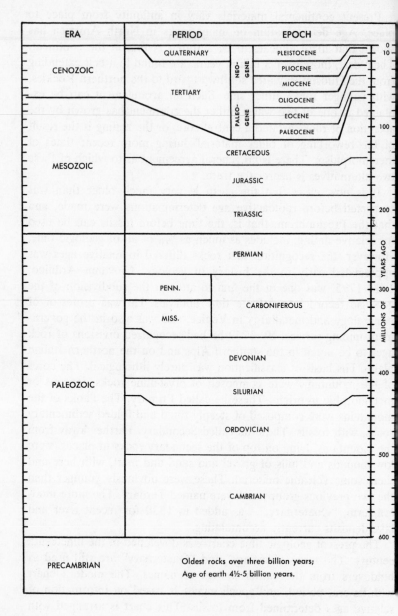

ERA	PERIOD	EPOCH	
CENOZOIC	QUATERNARY	NEO-GENE	PLEISTOCENE
			PLIOCENE
			MIOCENE
	TERTIARY	PALEO-GENE	OLIGOCENE
			EOCENE
			PALEOCENE
MESOZOIC	CRETACEOUS		
	JURASSIC		
	TRIASSIC		
PALEOZOIC	PERMIAN		
	CARBONIFEROUS	PENN.	
		MISS.	
	DEVONIAN		
	SILURIAN		
	ORDOVICIAN		
	CAMBRIAN		
PRECAMBRIAN	Oldest rocks over three billion years; Age of earth 4½-5 billion years.		

MILLIONS OF YEARS AGO

0
10

100

200

300

400

500

600

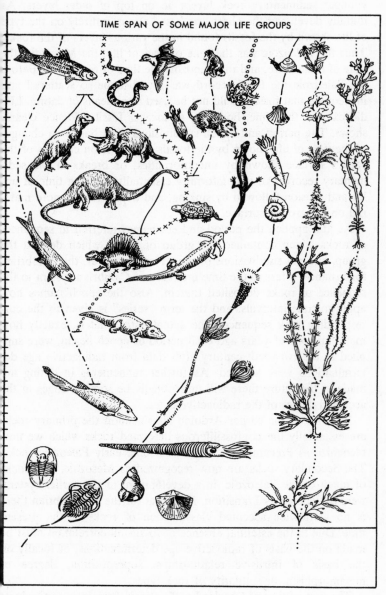

Age data from Kulp.

younger sedimentary rock layers lie on top of older layers. As initially developed the chart was based almost entirely on the type of life shown by the fossils found in the various layers of the rocks. Thus the Paleozoic was the time of ancient life, the Mesozoic, the time of middle life, and the Cenozoic the time of recent life. Before the Paleozoic the fossil record was found to be so scattered and inadequate that fossils could not be used as a means of dating. Life did exist at this time, however, as meager fossil evidence clearly shows. The period and epoch subdivisions were based on changes of the type of life shown by the fossils as well as on changes of the earth's surface shown by unconformities, or breaks in the sedimentary record. An uncomformity essentially marks a time of uplift and erosion followed by sinking, and deposition of more material on the eroded surface.

As first applied the period and era names referred to sequences of rocks which contained the group of fossils which defined the group, and not subdivisions of time. Now, however, the Cambrian, for instance, refers to the time interval and Cambrian system to the sequence of rocks deposited therein. Also the epoch names now apply to time intervals, and the term "series" is given to the corresponding rock sequence. The actual dates, that is, exactly how many millions of years ago each period or epoch began, were supplied in the twentieth century after data from radioactive age determinations were secured. As further refinements in dating are made in the future there will undoubtedly be some changes in the accepted values of the radioactive dates.

In terms of the earlier Arduino classification the primary rocks are essentially the nonfossiliferous deformed rocks which we now recognize as Precambrian, as well as some early Paleozoic rocks. The Secondary rocks are now recognized as Mesozoic. The rocks of much of the Paleozoic, in a development of the earlier system, were designated as Transition. Note that for the Precambrian there is no worldwide accepted classification of rocks at the present time. Due to the essential absence of fossils all correlation must be made on the basis of radioactive age determinations, or locally on the basis of intrusive relationships, superposition, degree of metamorphism, or similarity of rock types.

The first edition of Charles Lyell's classic *Principles of Geology*, which was completed in 1833, used the terms "Primary," "Secondary," and "Tertiary" and subdivided them into groups. Lyell used "Eocene," "Miocene," and "Pliocene" for subdivisions of the Tertiary, and "Cretaceous" and "Jura" were used in the Secondary. These terms are the only ones that he used which are still in the modern classification chart.

(Department of Commerce and Economic Development, Olympia, Washington)

Mount St. Helens, Washington. A strato-volcano in the Cascades

CHAPTER III

IGNEOUS ACTIVITY

Igneous activity in its outward forms is perhaps the most dramatic of the great earth-building processes. Volcanic eruptions of all types from small outpouring of lava to great fountains of liquid fire, and from mild detonations to cataclysmic explosions, are all manifestations of this process.

The areas of recent volcanic action are relatively limited. Sixty-two per cent of all active volcanoes lie on a ring encircling the Pacific Ocean, 45 per cent in the western Pacific area alone. This "Ring of Fire" is almost continuous. It runs up the western side of South America, and includes the volcanoes of the Andes, continues through Central America and Mexico with their numerous recent cones, thence northward through the Cascade Range of California, Oregon, and Washington into British Columbia. The cones, such as Mounts Lassen, Hood, St. Helens, Rainier, and Shasta, stand out as major landforms along this stretch of the western part of the United States. The volcanic zone continues through the Aleutian archipelago and includes peaks such as Mounts Katmai and Bogoslov, and thence down through the Japanese Islands to the Philippine Islands, Indonesia, and New Zealand.

In the Atlantic Ocean volcanic activity is far less extensive. It occurs in two separate localities, one along the Mid-Atlantic Ridge and the other in the West Indies, where Mont Pelée erupted early

in the present century. The parts of the Mid-Atlantic Ridge which
project above water, such as Iceland, the Azores, St. Peter and St.
Paul Rocks, Ascension Island, and Tristan da Cunha, are volcanic
in origin. Elsewhere in the world volcanic activity occurs in the
Hawaiian Islands, the Mediterranean zone of Italy and Sicily
which continues eastward through Asia Minor, and in Africa
where the major rift valleys have associated volcanoes such as
Mount Kilimanjaro. In the geologic past there was activity in many
other places, such as northern Europe and eastern United States,
as is shown by the presence of remnants such as buried lava flows
and volcanic necks. Igneous activity in any one area of the globe
has lasted for periods of 10 to 50 million years.

The visible forms of igneous activity are the lava flow and the
volcanic cone. A volcano consists of the conduit up which material
comes from depth and the edifice of extrusive material built
around this vent, whether it be composed of cinders, ash, blocks of
lava, or cooled liquids. Volcanoes are definitely not burning mountains, although a very insignificant amount of actual burning does
occur at times when, for instance, hydrogen gas combines with
oxygen. The appearance of burning is given by clouds of water
vapor and fine dust particles which look like smoke with the glow
from incandescent liquids and solids behind it.

The origin of volcanic craters was long open to question. Leo-
pold von Buch (1774-1853) thought that they were essentially
blisters of the crust which had broken open; that is, they were
formed when the surface layers were cracked open by some kind
of push from below. Sir Charles Lyell, however, in the middle of
the nineteenth century was the advocate of an opposing theory,
that volcanic cones resulted from the accumulation of material
extruded or blown out to the surface of the earth. Of course, as
soon as volcanically active areas were visited, and a more detailed
analysis of past volcanoes was made, it became obvious that the
accumulation of material was the true origin.

Gases, liquids, and solids all emerge in a volcanic eruption, and
depending on the preponderance of the type of material, fumarole,
lava flow, or cinder cone, respectively, may result. Volcanic solids
or pyroclastics (*pyro* from fire and *clastic* meaning broken), range
in size from particles of dust up to material measurable in tons.

Blocks of the crust or volcanic throat material may be broken and blown out. Volcanic bombs consist of new lava ejected as a liquid which solidifies in flight and lands in a pasty condition, flattening out when it hits the ground. While in the air these bombs may cool into fantastic shapes like teardrops or spindles with long thin tails, and they range in size from tons down to a few ounces. The smallest pyroclastic materials in decreasing size are cinders, ash, and dust. Much of this group is formed by the grinding together of fragments in the volcanic throat or by the disruption of larger, still liquid masses which are broken apart on emerging by the explosive pressure of dissolved gases. Volcanic solids, in general, fall close to the orifice from which they emerge, but the finer particles may be shot well up into the atmosphere and travel for miles. At the time when Krakatoa erupted in the East Indies on August 26, 1893, the fine volcanic dust rose into the upper atmosphere and spread around the world, causing some notable red sunsets, because of the scattering of sunlight by the fine particles. These sunsets were noticed first at Yuma, Arizona, on October 19, and in the eastern United States by October 30. They lasted for months before the dust finally settled to earth.

Liquid rock at depth is called magma, and once it reaches the surface it is known as lava. A distinction must be made here because the characteristics of a magma, while it still has all its dissolved gaseous material, is quite different from a lava from which the gases have largely escaped. The minimum temperature of still-liquid lava is generally between 800 and 1200 degrees C and is dependent on the chemical composition and the amount of volatiles present. Dissolved gases promote fluidity, and lavas which are richer in silicon and aluminum are more easily melted than those in which iron and magnesium are prominent.

The rate of cooling of a lava flow is remarkably slow. R. A. Daly in 1933 estimated that a three-foot layer of lava with an initial temperature of 1100 degrees C would cool on exposure to the air to 750 degrees C in ten days. If the lava were 30 feet thick it would take three years to cool, and if it were 300 feet thick it would take 30 years. Of course the time to cool down to 100 degrees C, the temperature of boiling water, would take much longer. The cooled frothy crust on the surface of a lava forms an excellent insulator and keeps the heat from being dissipated rapidly. It was reported that the Vesuvius flow of 1785 was still steaming after seven years, yet lichens were growing on the surface.

The composition of gases emitted from volcanic eruptions varies considerably. In most cases, however, water forms by far the largest proportion. The composition of the gas in one of the typical

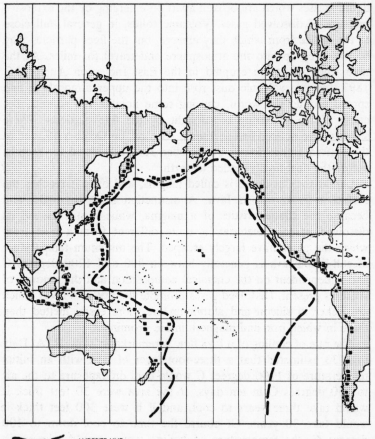

- - - - -   ANDESITE LINE
• - • - •   RECENTLY ACTIVE VOLCANOES

Hawaiian eruptions was as follows: 79.31 per cent water, 11.61 per cent carbon dioxide, 6.48 per cent sulfur dioxide, 1.29 per cent nitrogen, 0.58 per cent hydrogen, 0.37 per cent carbon monoxide, 0.24 per cent sulfur, 0.05 per cent chlorine, and 0.04 per cent argon. It is thought that such volcanic gases represent at least in part new material reaching the earth's surface for the first time, and that over long geological periods this primordial gaseous ma-

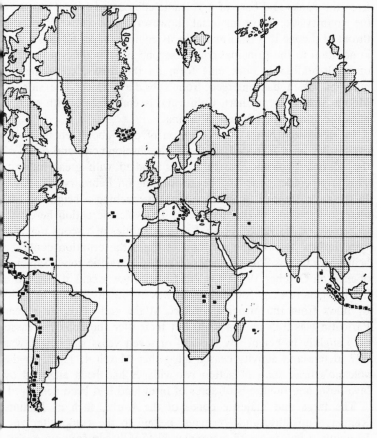

Recently active volcanoes of the world. Sixty-two per cent lie on the circumpacific "Ring of Fire."

terial has been the source for the present atmosphere and for the water in the seas.

There are three types of volcanic cone: the cinder cone, composed primarily of solids; the shield cone made up largely of flows; and the strato-volcano or composite cone, an intermediate type built up by alternating flows and ash falls. One type may merge into another and it may be difficult to decide into what category a single example should be put, since liquids at times emerge from a cinder cone and solids from a shield volcano. Flows often emerge from the flanks and base of a volcanic edifice and spread out over the countryside. Most material, however, must come from the throat of a cone if it is to maintain its conical shape. Occasionally, in addition to the principal cone a second or sometimes a number of small additional ones may form on the flanks, composed of material which has emerged from subsidiary exits. The side of Mount Shasta, in northern California, is embellished with such a parasitic cone called Mount Shastina.

In all written history, the creation of only about ten new volcanoes has been recorded, so the birth, development, and death of the Mexican volcano Parícutin was studied with great interest. This large cinder cone first began forming on February 20, 1943. In the early stages it grew very rapidly, reaching a height of 140 meters at the end of the first week. The volcanic action here was extremely explosive and noisy. Large quantities of viscous material were hurled high in the air, and at times the eruption could be heard as much as 350 kilometers away. A parasitic cone, Sapichu, opened on October 19, 1943, and within a few weeks it reached a height of more than 100 meters. It was eventually buried in 1946 by flows from the principal orifice. At the end of the first year Parícutin was 325 meters high, but thereafter the cone increased only slightly in height. By the end of seven years the height was 397 meters and activity ceased altogether March 4, 1952. In the volcano's brief span of action two villages had been engulfed by lava flows and hundreds of acres of farm land had been destroyed.

The large and majestic cones of the world, such as Mounts Rainier, Fujiyama, and Vesuvius, belong to the composite type. Vesuvius, a volcano with a complex history, began forming probably about 10,000 years ago. It was already very old at the time of the classic eruption of A.D. 79, which resulted in the destruction of Pompeii and Herculaneum and which was described in the letters of Pliny the Younger. Vesuvius is on a line of volcanoes which stretches northward from Naples toward Siena. The construction of a strato-volcano such as Vesuvius, or of a shield cone, may take many thousands of years, in striking contrast to the tens of years at most needed to build up a typical small cinder cone.

Shield volcanoes are very large, and low compared with their width, having a characteristic shield-shaped profile seen from a distance. The Hawaiian volcanoes which belong to this type are classic examples. As seen from the sea the cones rise in low wide arches. The currently active volcanoes are all on the Island of Hawaii which lies at the southeast end of a long submarine ridge which extends approximately 1,600 miles to the Kure Islands on the northwest and includes Midway Island. The Hawaiian ridge is an isolated volcanic region 2,000 miles away from any other tectonically active area, and follows a major fracture in the crust through which lava has come from a source of magma at depth. Volcanic activity started in the northwest and migrated in time to the southeast. The northwestern islands have long since ceased to be volcanically active, and are now but wave-eroded fragments and remnants of their former selves.

Mauna Loa, the largest active volcano on Hawaii, rises 13,680 feet above sea level and more than 30,000 feet above the sea floor, and has a total volume of more than 10,000 cubic miles. The rate of growth of such a cone is rapid. Intervals between eruptions are only a few years or decades, and the flanks of the active volcanoes are blanketed by new flows so rapidly that erosion makes little headway.

In November and December of 1959 a typical eruption occurred at Kilauea Iki, a vent within a mile of the major Kilauea crater. Before the eruption, during October, several small shallow earthquakes were reported every day, and tilt meters showed a bulging of the surface of the volcano as they had done before the earlier eruption of 1955. When used on the flank of a volcano, a tilting away from the crater indicates the intrusion of magma into the heart of the cone moderately close to the surface. The magma here is known to have originated 40 to 60 kilometers down, in the upper part of the mantle. This melted rock was less dense than the surrounding solid material, and moved up into the overlying rocks, eventually accumulating at a depth of a few kilometers below the crater. Final eruption was accompanied by small-scale earth tremors caused by the rapid flow of magma through the conduits leading from the upper accumulating zone to the surface. Lava fountains rose to a height of 1,600 feet or more; and after each phase of activity much lava flowed back into the vent, sometimes as much as 10 million cubic yards at a time. There was, however, a net gain made in the level of the lava lake after each time of eruption.

The bulging of a cone may not necessarily mean an eruption at the crater, since lava may reach the surface on the flanks. In this fashion the pressure is greatly relieved and the cone may return to normal without any eruption out of the crater at all. In the Hawaiian cone there has been a rough alternation between eruptions at or near the summit and those down on the flanks.

Much of the bulk of shield cones is built by flows which emerge along fractures that follow rift zones. Erosion has exposed these zones in some of the older inactive cones down to a depth of 4,000 feet and they presumably go down several miles. Hundreds of closely spaced dikes now mark the formerly active rifts. Fissure eruptions several hundred to some thousands of feet long have occurred on both Kilauea and Mauna Loa, and one must imagine a network of fractures connecting the surface eruptions with magma at depth.

The velocity of flowing lava varies greatly. In very unusual cases speeds up to 25 m.p.h. have been measured on Hawaii, especially where flow is on steep slopes and confined to a narrow channel. At Parícutin 50 feet per minute near the source on steep slopes was clocked, and a mile away from the source and on gentler slopes 50 feet an hour was measured.

A volcanic eruption can be predicted under certain conditions. Some deep earthquakes are due to the movement of magma in the upper part of the mantle, and many shallow earthquakes and the tilting of the slopes on a cone mean that the magma is moving around fairly close to the surface, and an eruption may be imminent. Another way of predicting the possible coming of an eruption is by detecting the presence of hot lava near the surface by means of airborne thermal instruments which are sensitive to infrared rays. Such heat waves have been mapped in connection with volcanic activity on Kilauea.

The shape of the upper accumulation chamber under a Hawaiian volcano is probably lenticular in form and lies about five kilometers below the top of the mountain. This information comes from an analysis of earthquake waves due to the movement of magma at that depth. In other places the depths to the accumulation chambers have been calculated in a variety of ways. At Vesuvius lava accumulated probably about six kilometers down. This is indicated by the presence of small fragments of altered dolomite of Triassic age brought up in the lava. The depth to this dolomite is known and thus the depth to the magma. The Japanese volcano Mihara has an accumulation chamber about five kilometers down. This was calculated from local changes in magnetism attributed to changes in temperature within the magma chamber.

The summit craters of the Hawaiian volcanoes are enormous, many miles across, and should strictly be called calderas. True explosive craters rarely exceed ¾ to one mile in diameter, whereas calderas are well over a mile wide. They are primarily due to engulfment, that is, to the flow of magma back down into the throat of a volcano and thence into the accumulation chamber. This return flow causes a collapse of the top of the cone and thus enlargement of the crater.

Crater Lake in Oregon lies in a classic example of a caldera. The lake is nearly circular, six miles across, 2,000 feet deep and surrounded by cliffs 500 to 2,000 feet high. The caldera here resulted from the partial destruction of the original volcano, Mount Mazama, following a very violent eruption when the top was blown off. This self-decapitation was followed by collapse. The volume of material which disappeared is approximately 17 cubic miles. It has been calculated that not more than 7½ cubic miles of rock were thrown out at the time of the major eruption, leaving presumably ten cubic miles to be engulfed following a retreat of the lava back down into the cone. Undoubtedly room was made for this lava by a shift of magma at a still greater depth.

Wizard Island, which protrudes 780 feet above lake level, is the top of a cinder cone formed after the production of the caldera.

Volcanic eruptions vary widely in their explosiveness, from those of extreme violence to those where lava appears quietly at the surface. The greatest volcanic explosion in historic time took place at Krakatoa in Indonesia (then the East Indies), during an eruption which destroyed practically the entire island with its 2,700-foot summit and blasted a hole 1,000 feet deep in the ocean floor. The noise of the explosion was heard 3,000 miles away on Rodriquez Island near Madagascar.

The most explosive type of eruption is called peléean, after Mont Pelée. Its distinguishing characteristic is a glowing cloud of hot pumice which shoots out very suddenly and is highly destructive. At the foot of Mont Pelée, the town of St. Pierre with a population of 25,000 was entirely destroyed in a few minutes by such a peléean cloud in 1902. In 1912 a very violent eruption took place in the Alaskan Peninsula which blew off half of Katmai volcano and left a hole in the ground large enough to hold all the buildings of Greater New York. During this eruption a valley five miles northwest of the volcano was filled by an incandescent flow of pumice, sand and ash, thus producing the Valley of Ten Thousand Smokes, so called because of the vast number of fumaroles. No lava is extruded during a peléean eruption except at times in a very viscous state in the crater itself. On Mont Pelée, after the eruption of 1902 a mass of lava was slowly extruded, and cooled so quickly that it stood straight up as a vertical spine in the crater. It soon broke up and disappeared because of its instability.

Vulcanean eruptions, named after the island of Vulcano off Sicily, consist of the emission of relatively thick and pasty lava, following the formation of a thick crust in the crater after rather infrequent eruptions. Eruptions here are strongly explosive and the cone may sometimes be partially destroyed. Broken fragments and some new scoria are blown out, and often, a large cauliflower-shaped cloud of ash is formed. After the initial explosion lava may emerge from the flanks. Vesuvius has this type of eruption. Vulcano, the type example, was last active in 1889-1890.

A somewhat less destructive type of eruption is the Strombolian, named after Mount Stromboli, off Sicily. This mountain, known as the "Lighthouse of the Mediterranean," has explosions of moderate intensity, and emits pasty, often incandescent, scoria-type lava, accompanied by a white cloud. The Hawaiian type of eruption is still less explosive. Abundant lava of the dark basaltic type is emitted. Moderate amounts of gases are liberated, although at times lava fountains may shoot up to a height of a thousand feet or so.

The primary force in producing any explosive type of eruption is the presence of gases, chiefly very hot water vapor under very high pressure which will expand in an explosive fashion as soon as magma reaches the surface. When there is essentially no gas present the least explosive of all types of eruption occurs. Many of the lava flows in Iceland are characteristic of this type, where lava appears relatively quietly and oozes out of fissures in the ground.

The Icelandic type of eruption showed its greatest historical development in continental United States in the Columbia Plateau. This area covers approximately 200,000 square miles, and the volume of basalt which has been extruded is in the order of magnitude of 100,000 cubic miles. In many places the combined thicknesses of the various lava flows total 3,000 feet; individual flows however rarely exceed 30 to 100 feet in thickness. A similar and equally large area of lava flows occurs in the Deccan Plateau of India. In both cases the lava welled out of the ground along extensive fissures, at times miles in length, one flow following another through a history extending over millions of years.

The Columbia Plateau lies in eastern Oregon and Washington and in southern Idaho. Flows here started emerging in early Tertiary times, and swamped an area where the relief was measured in some thousands of feet. They continued periodically throughout the Tertiary up into very recent times. In southern Idaho, at the Craters of the Moon National Monument, cinder cones, small cones built up by spattering gouts of lava, and flows, all largely unweathered, show how recently activity occurred here.

The surface characteristics of basalt lava flows vary from place to place rather widely. Sometimes the surface is composed of large blocks of porous lava formed when a cooled crust was broken by a hot, still-moving mass of lava underneath. This gives the so-called aa type of lava. The aa flow results in a wild disarray of angular jagged fragments, so very irregular that traveling over the surface is extremely difficult. In contrast to this, one can find in places a surface which is smoothly rounded, billowy looking, with pleats, wrinkles, and ruffled structures—the pahoehoe type of flow. The upper parts of such basalt flows are commonly scoriaceous, that is,

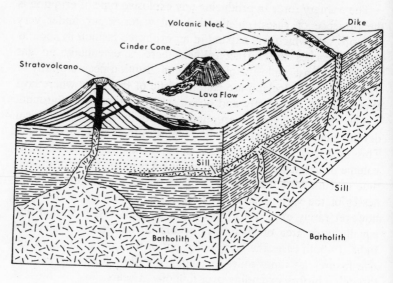

Igneous rock forms; extrusive and intrusive

full of bubble holes. Often these bubble holes are pulled out and elongated as the stiff lava oozes just before solidifying. Pahoehoe, the corded type, develops where a skin covers the still molten mass below. The liquid lava cools and the skin wrinkles. If the liquid drains away, tubes and tunnels may result. Occasionally these tunnels form large caves some tens of feet high and a hundred feet long. Liquid lava dripping from the ceilings may build short stalactites.

Altogether there is a fantastic variety of detailed features to be found in lava flows. Collapse depressions, a few feet up to thousands of feet across, may be formed by the falling in of the roofs of lava tunnels. Elsewhere the surface may be squeezed up into knobby protuberances and ridges as lava under renewed pressure tries to make room for itself beneath a surface previously cooled and hardened. If a flow invades an area of trees and if the lava is relatively cool it may solidify before the trees are entirely burned, and thus tree molds will be left.

In many places the earlier flows of the Columbia Plateau have been incised by rivers and the edge of the lava sheets is exposed to view, revealing columnar jointing very clearly. This type of jointing develops when a lava flow cools. Contraction accompanies the cooling, and since a flow covering a large area cannot contract laterally as a whole, it will break up into vertical cracks separating polygonal columns. Columnar jointing is especially characteristic of basalt.

The underground movement of magma and the shapes into which it cools on entering cracks and crevices in the rocks cannot of course be observed while actually occurring. After cooling and the weathering and erosion of all the material which covered them at one time, however, such intrusive bodies become exposed to view, and their various shapes and sizes can be noted and studied. Such evidence for past igneous activity is to be found in the rocks in many areas not now volcanically active.

Magma may freeze into a variety of shapes varying greatly in size. Dikes are relatively small intrusive bodies cutting across pre-existing rocks which may be sedimentary, metamorphic, or previous igneous rock itself. On erosion such dikes will be obvious since they are composed of material different in color and texture from that of the host rock. All dikes are of course younger than the rocks into which they are intruded.

Sills are igneous bodies which have been intruded between and are parallel to pre-existing layered rocks. In this respect they may resemble lava flows, later buried under layers of sediments. When a sill is intruded it is hot, and will slightly alter the rocks both above and below it. On the other hand, a lava flow will metamorphose only the material underneath it, there being none above it as yet. Furthermore, a sill may project in places with minor tongues of lava into the overlying material. In other words, a sill may change into a dike here and there at its margin, both above and below. The Palisades of the Hudson River is an especially good example of a sill. It shows just such intrusive relationships at its upper margin as well as evidence of having baked the overlying sediments. The term "palisades" comes from the obvious large-scale columnar jointing. The Watchung Mountains in New Jersey, on the other hand, are excellent examples of buried and then re-exposed lava flows, revealed by the erosion of the overlying material. The lava flows in this case are tilted somewhat toward the west with the result that these resistant rocks now form ridges with a gentle westward slope and a steep scarp facing east.

Magma in the neck of a volcano may freeze and this material may perhaps be all the evidence left for the existence of a former cone, once the cone itself has been entirely eroded away. Volcanic necks, often more resistant than the material into which they were intruded, may stand up as small angular hills, such as Ship Rock in the northwest corner of New Mexico. There are also a number of dikes which radiate from Ship Rock and now form ridges extending outward from the central neck itself. These dikes are composed of volcanic material which left the neck and penetrated the surrounding rocks. Volcanic skeletons of the intrusive type, or extrusive types which have been buried, thus may control the development of scenery for millions of years after igneous activity has ceased altogether.

A very large mass of magma cooled slowly at depth forms a batholith. The Sierra Nevada Mountains are composed of a granite batholith which is now exposed to view following extensive erosion, after uplift and tilting of this section of the crust.

The role that igneous activity has played in the development of the crust of the earth was not generally appreciated before the beginning of the nineteenth century. Near the end of the eighteenth century James Hutton developed the concept of a major genetic class of rocks, formed in the depths of the crust by the crystallization of material from the molten state. He grouped these with the volcanic rocks which appeared at the surface and called them igneous. As a matter of fact he included a few rocks now known to be sedimentary in his igneous classification. A key observation in the development of his theory was made by Hutton in 1785 in Scotland, where he found a granite which, on intruding a limestone layer, had by its heat very obviously altered it.

Opposed to Hutton's vulcanist philosophy was that of the Neptunists who maintained that granite and many other rocks which we now know to be igneous were deposited from a universal ocean. Abraham Gottlieb Werner, a teacher in the School of Mines in Freiburg, was a strong advocate of this philosophy. Born in 1749, he taught mineralogy and mining and insisted that all rocks were sedimentary in origin. He suggested that the earth started as a muddy blob and that the rocks therefore were sedimentary. He did, however, admit that some volcanoes existed, but thought that in this case the heat was due to burning coal. He was such a brilliant teacher and talked so persuasively of his subject that he thoroughly convinced his pupils of the Neptunist point of view. Many of these, however, after traveling around the countryside investigating various igneous rocks, had to change to a vulcanist viewpoint when they saw the volcanoes of France and the clear evidence of the intrusive nature of dikes and sills. The dominance of Werner's Neptunist views and the obstinate adherence to them by many of his pupils led to violent controversy between these two schools of thought and undoubtedly stimulated much field work and the gathering of data, before the true nature of the origin of rocks was eventually worked out.

Devil's Postpile, California. Columnar jointing in a basalt lava flow

CHAPTER IV

IGNEOUS ROCKS

Magmas, the source of all igneous rocks, are essentially very high temperature melts, in which the constituents are mutually dissolved. They can be thought of as mixtures of randomly dispersed atoms and groups of atoms, which sort themselves out, as the magma cools, according to chemical affinities and sizes to produce various minerals. Each of the resulting mineral species has its own definite chemical and physical properties which distinguish it from others. Some are made up of only one chemical element, but usually minerals are a combination of different elements. The three-dimensional arrangement of the atoms or atomic groups is a regular one in almost all minerals and results in what is called a crystalline structure. If the different atoms are not arranged in such a definite geometric pattern the structure is amorphous.

All rocks, it should be noted, whether they be igneous, sedimentary, or metamorphic, are composed of aggregates of minerals. Sometimes, only one kind of mineral is present, as in limestone, which is composed of interlocking calcium carbonate crystals. Generally, however, there is a variety of different mineral species in a rock.

Magmas are geologically temporary, local pockets of melted material in the crust and upper parts of the earth's mantle. They have no connection whatever with the molten core of the earth; earthquake waves demonstrate conclusively that the crust and mantle act as though they were solid, and thus the accumulation of magma must be very small and insignificant when compared with the earth as a whole.

The development of magma is probably due to a greater concentration of heat locally, perhaps from a radioactive source, and relief in pressure. It has been observed that everywhere the temperature of the earth rises as one goes deeper and deeper. In extrapolating this so-called thermal gradient downward it does not take many miles before the temperature of the rocks is hot enough to form a magma. The melting point of rock, however, is raised by pressure, so that material hot enough to be liquid at the earth's surface will still remain a solid at depth. To melt, a solid must expand, but expansion is difficult under such high pressure. Relief of pressure will allow a potential magma, that is, a rock hot enough to be magma if it were less compressed, to melt. Magmas are generally associated with areas of active crustal disturbance of earthquakes and mountains. Once a magma is formed it is less dense than the solid rock around it and tends to move to a place of less pressure, generally upward. It may eat its way by melting and incorporating the overlying solid rock, it may wedge the nearer surface rocks apart, or it may infiltrate along fractures or bedding planes. On reaching the surface the magma becomes lava and gives rise to various volcanic extrusives, as we have seen.

The temperature of the magma may be well below the freezing temperatures of any one of the constituent minerals before final solidification occurs. This situation is similar to what happens in a mixture of salt and water which will not freeze until below the freezing point of water. The solution of one material in another results in a lower freezing point than exhibited by the constituents separately. Actually the order of crystallization of the minerals from a magma is determined by solubility in the magma rather than fusibility, or the temprature at which the separate constituents melt as isolated minerals. For instance, it can be noted that in a granite, which is composed essentially of quartz and feldspar, the quartz is formed last. However, quartz by itself has a higher melting point than feldspar and should seemingly form first as a magma is cooled. For this reason, the Neptunists concluded that granite could not have cooled from a melt. They did not realize as we do now that the order of crystallization in an igneous rock is controlled by solubility.

A detailed investigation of igneous rocks shows hundreds of varieties, which differ in color, texture, and composition. However, by far the most common are the dark-colored extrusive basalt and the light-colored intrusive granite. Thus, in general, two great classes of magma must exist. The basaltic rocks are relatively much richer in the diagnostic elements iron and magnesium, and poorer in sodium, potassium, and silica than granite.

Tremendous accumulations of basalt have been piled up in the Hawaiian chain of islands, in total up to perhaps 100,000 cubic miles. The Columbia Plateau represents an accumulation, as we have seen, of about 100,000 cubic miles and the Deccan Plateau in India somewhat more. It has been suggested that the basaltic kind of magma originates in the upper part of the mantle by the melting of the rock there which is considered to be similar in chemical composition but perhaps with a different group of minerals, more in keeping with the high-pressure environment.

The composition of the continental rocks of the crust is markedly different from that of the crustal rocks underneath the ocean basins. Continental material, called sial, is less dense and has a higher proportion of silica. "Sial" is a word coined to signify silicon and aluminum. Granite and rocks of similar composition are typical continental rocks. Denser material richer in magnesium and iron underlying the ocean basins has been given the name "sima," which stands for silicon and magnesium. Basalt is the most common, characteristic rock of the sima. The composition of the upper mantle apparently is similar to that of oceanic rocks.

In general the continental volcanoes emit sialic-type lavas such as rhyolite and andesite, and the oceanic volcanoes are basalt-producing. A clear line can be drawn through the western Pacific which divides the basalt volcanoes of the central part of the Pacific Basin from the andesite volcanoes of the Asian continent. This so-called Andesite Line separates Japan, Fiji, the Philippines, and Australia, which lie on the continental side, from Hawaii, Samoa, Pitcairn, Marcus Island, and a host of submerged cones, which are basalt-producing. On the eastern side of the Pacific Basin the Andesite Line essentially follows the continental borders. Other ocean basins do not show a similar clear division.

The same volcano at different times may emit different kinds of igneous rocks, and the question arises whether a variety of magma sources have been tapped. The explanation for this phenomenon at least in part may lie, however, in the process of magmatic differentiation, or the splitting of an originally homogeneous magma into components with dissimilar chemical compositions. This may be accomplished by fractional crystallization, in which the minerals which first crystallize may be heavy and drop to the bottom of a magma mass, thus leaving the composition of the remaining liquid unlike the original. If volcanic eruptions occur before and after such differentiation the type of lava which is emitted will of course reflect the change in magma composition. The Palisades Sill of New York and New Jersey affords an excellent example of this type of differentiation. Near the base of the sill is a layer which has been enriched by the mineral olivine. The olivine was crystallized out of the melt early, and left the remaining liquid with a composition somewhat different from what it had initially. In general the minerals which crystallize first are those with higher percentages of iron, magnesium, and calcium, leaving a liquid impoverished in these elements and thus enriched by comparison in other elements or those which have not been removed.

A magma may also change its composition by melting parts of the rock which it is intruding, or different magmas may mingle and the resulting mixture may thus have a composition different from that of either one initially. Any basaltic magma which rises from the mantle can be contaminated with various amounts of sialic material from the continental crust as it eats its way to the surface.

The diversity of igneous rocks depends on two factors, variations in chemical composition, as we have just seen, and variations in the environment in which the rock has cooled. The environment determines the texture of the resulting rock, whether it is coarse-grained, fine-grained or glassy. If a mass of lava cools very quickly it will form a glassy rock. This happens because the atoms composing the liquid are not given a chance to form specific minerals or chemical compounds, but are frozen into any random arrangement they might be in at the time; in other words, the structure is amorphous. Under less rapid cooling, however, initial crystals of minerals are given a chance to grow by the addition of atoms or groups of atoms one after the other. Such a process, on very slow cooling, leads to relatively coarse-grained rocks. Thus extrusive rocks, because of their rapid rate of cooling are glassy or perhaps fine-grained, while intrusive rocks are never glassy and tend to be coarser-grained.

Each major clan of igneous rocks, the generally light-colored or sialic, and the generally dark-colored or simatic, has representa-

RATE OF COOLING	TEXTURE	LIGHT-COLORED MINERALS DOMINATE (SIALIC)		DARK-COLORED MINERALS DOMINATE (SIMATIC)
Slow	Coarse-grained	Granite		Gabbro
Rapid	Fine-grained	Rhyolite	Andesite	Basalt
Very Rapid	Glass Froth	Pumice		Scoria
	Glass	Obsidian		

Simplified chart of the igneous rocks

tives which have cooled in each environment.

Granite masses in the form of batholiths many thousands of square miles in extent form the largest comparatively homogeneous bodies of rock accessible to man. They are found only on continents, never in oceanic areas. Granite is closely associated in both times and space with mountain-building and with regional metamorphism in areas where there are very thick sequences of sedimentary rocks and volcanics, that is, in geosynclines. In many mountain areas deep erosion has uncovered large batholiths of granite, and in some of the large, older regions of the continents, such as the Shield area of Canada, the roots of ancient mountains are exposed, revealing metamorphic rocks shot through with masses of granite, forming so-called mixed rocks or migmatites. In some places granite has obviously intruded as a liquid into other rocks which may show metamorphic changes as a result. In other places metamorphic rocks of obvious sedimentary origin grade laterally into mixed rocks and these in turn into granite. Also granite may in places contain structures and relicts which line up with neighboring metamorphic rocks. The Chelmsford granite in eastern Massachusetts still shows traces of the original bedding and folds of its undoubted sedimentary rock ancestor.

A number of theories concerning the origin of granite has understandably been formulated to explain the observations. Perhaps different granites have somewhat different origins and the problem facing the geologist concerns the origin of a specific granite, not all granites.

The classic igneous rock theory for granite assumes that it was formed by magmatic differentiation from a basaltic magma. In order to produce the tremendously large granite areas of the world, however, it would have required what most geologists consider fantastically large volumes of simatic magma.

Another theory is that granite has resulted from the metamorphism of other rocks, usually sedimentary, by the action of hot solutions coming up through them or by the intergranular migration of atoms or groups of atoms from elsewhere. Obviously not all new materials need necessarily be brought in, but just enough to change the pre-existing composition to that of granite. Also unwanted material would of course have to be removed. The suggestion has also been made that a granite is due to the melting, in a water environment, of rocks with the proper chemical composition for granite followed by the crystallization of this material *in situ,* with perhaps some squeezing into neighboring rocks to give cases of real intrusive contacts. An average sequence of sedimentary rocks has the proper composition for the extraction of granite liquids from heterogeneous rocks by selective fusion and solution. According to this suggestion, batholiths are formed in the deeper parts of the geosynclinal areas where the temperatures are high enough and water is present in the proper amount. It has been calculated that at depths between 12 and 20 kilometers where the temperature gradient is in the order of 30 degrees C per kilometer depth, complete melting of material of the proper composition should occur if between 9 and 10 per cent water is available. In this explanation for the formation of granite each major mountain range must have its own granite roots, formed at the time that the mountain was given its structure.

The close genetic connection between igneous rocks and mineral deposits has long been apparent. It has often been said that magmas are the parents, mineral deposits the offspring. In the southwestern parts of the United States extensive deposits of copper are associated with intrusive igneous rocks. The ore minerals have been deposited along large faults apparently from solutions coming up from a magma at depth. Also mined in this area are lead, zinc, silver, and gold.

From the standpoint of the origin of mineral deposits, an interesting well was drilled in 1961-1962 in the Salton Sea area of the Imperial Valley, California. The well was drilled to a depth of 5,232 feet and it tapped hot water very rich in a variety of heavy metals and various rare elements. The temperature was between 270 and 300 degrees C and it has been suggested that the water might be purely magmatic in origin and be an active ore-forming solution actually encountered at depth. It was very rich in potassium, and lithium, and such metals as copper, iron, silver, cobalt, chromium, lead, tin, antimony, strontium, and vanadium were found. Such magmatic water with its metallic content is thought to be the last remnants of a freezing magma and to be the source for the ore deposits associated with igneous rocks.

There are a number of questions involving igneous rocks which still puzzle geologists. The complete story of granite is certainly one, and others concern themselves with the place and origin of magma in general, the mechanics by which magmas rise to the surface, the various processes which lead to the range in magma composition, as yet understood in their broadest outlines only, and the detailed subsurface structure of volcano systems. And perhaps most fundamental, Why do volcanoes occur where they do at the present time and why does the location of igneous activity change from place to place throughout geologic time?

(National Park Service)

Liberty Cap, Yosemite Valley, California. Exfoliation dome

CHAPTER V

WEATHERING AND
MASS-WASTING

Following the creation of any new land surface either by volcanic activity or by diastrophic forces, the processes of weathering and erosion start to work immediately to modify it, and in so doing create the almost unlimited variety of scenery which we see around us.

Solid rock must first be weathered, that is, broken into small fragments, before effective transfer by the agents of erosion can occur. The mass transfer of material down slopes under the direct force of gravity, so-called mass-wasting, is a great aid in the work of transportation.

Wherever there is the slightest slope the surface of the land is in a spasmodic state of motion, slipping, sliding, and creeping down-hill. When sudden and dramatic, such motion results in landslides, rockfalls, and slumps. Less obvious features result from the slower process of soil creep. In some places generations may come and go and the shape of the land may remain to all outward appearances the same. Nevertheless, even here there is a constant turmoil of atoms and groups of atoms forever rearranging themselves in fresh combinations, in an invisible microscopic world. Eventually such changes on the microscopic level will become obvious, and a change in the contour of the land is visible. Certainly the world around us and the landscape with its myriad modifications has an interest which a static and unchanging scene would lack.

Running water and the mass movement of debris always carry material downhill, and the topographic forms which result therefrom are conditioned by this fact. On the other hand, glaciers and the wind may sometimes carry material up slopes and leave hills and mounds of debris at a slightly higher elevation than it started. However, the over-all tendency here also is to move material downhill.

Erosion is a dynamic process, one of pickup, of transfer and then eventual dumping of debris. Weathering, in contrast, is a static process, and consists of the breaking up of solid rock into fragments, either by chemical changes or mechanical disintegration. It is the response of minerals and rocks to the environment of the earth's surface.

Weathering and its relative rapidity are abundantly clear to anyone who notes the blurred inscription on an old gravestone, the rotting foundations of an old building, or the crumbling of concrete roads and sidewalks. Often a deep roadcut will uncover the transition from hard, fresh rock at the bottom through more and more discolored and crumbly material to soil at the surface. In all these cases the evidence of decay and fragmentation is obvious. Such destruction is due to a variety of processes, such as temperature changes, frost action, or chemically active solutions. The rate of weathering, which varies greatly from place to place, is dependent on the climate and the type of rock. It is relatively slow in warm dry climate, but in warm humid areas chemical changes can be very rapid and important and at places where the temperature varies both above and below the freezing point frost-wedging plays a vital part in the disruption of rocks.

If weathered material is not removed, rock decomposition may extend to great depths. South of the glaciated areas of the United States the depth of decayed rock is markedly greater than in the glaciated areas themselves, where it is difficult in places to find any rotted rock, since it has been removed by the very strong abrasive and plucking action of the ice which overrode the land in the very recent geologic past. Usually, even in unglaciated areas, decayed rock is not found to a depth of more than a few tens of feet;

however, under ideal conditions of warm humid climates and in areas where removal has been very slow, such as some tropical regions in Brazil, weathered rock has been found over 400 feet at depth.

Chemical weathering or decomposition primarily involves the recombination of rock materials with oxygen, carbon dioxide, and water vapor present in the earth's atmosphere, to form fresh compounds more in keeping with the conditions of temperature, pressure, and chemistry prevailing at the surface. Carbon dioxide in combination with water produces weak carbonic acid, and vegetation supplies various organic acids which also greatly aid in rock decomposition.

Some rock minerals are far more susceptible to change than others. In a granite, for instance, the quartz is relatively stable in comparison with the feldspars, which are very quickly changed into a series of new compounds, specifically clay, a soluble carbonate, and quartz. Collectively these products occupy a much greater volume than the initial feldspar, and this change can result in a strong disruptive force, tending to break up the rock. Furthermore, the three-dimensional interlocking network of quartz, feldspar, and mica crystals is destroyed so that all that remains is a loosely aggregated pile of fragments. Any rock containing iron-bearing minerals will, on weathering, produce various iron oxides, generally the hydrous variety, limonite, which frequently forms a yellow-brown stain on the surface. Some rocks, such as limestone (calcium carbonate), are merely dissolved by acidic groundwater and carried away in solution.

Mechanical weathering or disintegration does not create new minerals but does aid chemical weathering by creating more surface areas on which chemical changes can occur. Frost-wedging is especially effective in temperate and polar regions where temperature changes cause frequent freeze-and-thaw cycles. Water expands approximately 9 per cent on changing to ice, and thus water which enters any cracks in a rock ledge will, on freezing, lead to the fragmentation of an otherwise solid mass of rock. Tree roots growing in cracks in a rock will enlarge and may split it open. Other agents of disintegration include the sudden heat of forest fires, and perhaps the shock and heat of lightning striking rock outcrops. The daily heating and cooling of a ledge of rock should logically cause disintegration, but evidence for the effectiveness of this is inconclusive. For example, the minerals in a granite are known to expand and contract at different rates with changes of temperature, and after many such heating and cooling cycles should break apart. However, experiments in which a granite has been artificially heated and cooled enough times to equal some hundreds of years of exposure to the sun have produced no noticeable fracturing.

One of the most obvious topographic forms associated with weathering is the exfoliation dome, which is ideally developed in relatively massive granite where the major vertical joints are widely spaced. Such a rounded, glistening dome of rock often many hundreds of feet across is formed by the peeling off of thin sheets of stone along broadly curved joints which are more or less parallel to the rock surface. These joints are characteristically only a few inches apart near the surface and increase to several feet apart deeper in the rock. The origin of these features is believed to be due in large part to relief of pressure, following the removal of overlying material by erosion. Such a history will result in an expansion of the outer parts of the rock and thus lead to the development of such curved fractures, which are more closely spaced near the surface where the confining pressure is least. Support for this suggestion is supplied by the measurable expansion of large granite blocks after their removal from a quarry. Furthermore, the expansion due to some chemical change in the surface layers, such as the breakup of feldspars, may be an important contributing factor. Exfoliation domes are found beautifully developed in Yosemite Park in California.

A type of weathering which produces somewhat similar results, but on a much smaller scale, forms rounded boulders by the spalling off of concentric layers of weathered rock. These residual boulders are developed in place and may form in any relatively massive rock which is cut by a series of joints, both vertical and horizontal. Granite, diorite, and gabbro are especially susceptible to this type of weathering. Such blocks of rocks outlined by cracks will be chemically changed along the cracks, the decomposition of the feldspars being especially important here. Inasmuch as the attack will be from two sides along the edges and three at the corners, an initially roughly rectangular block will become rounded in the course of time. Often only a hard unweathered core remains, which is surrounded by crumbly layers and mineral frag-

Evidences of slope instability: slump, soil creep shown by tilted trees, poles, and posts.

ments. Yosemite Park in California shows good examples of this type of weathering also. Hard granite boulders up to a number of feet in diameter may be found enmeshed in rotted granite which breaks into many small mineral fragments when attacked with nothing more potent than a pointed stick.

Topographic features associated with mass-wasting are especially notable where steep slopes and cliffs are present. In mountainous areas, landslides, rockfalls, and piles of rocky debris at the base of cliffs, talus slopes—all attest to the rapid downhill sliding and slipping of fragments, loosened initially by disintegration or decomposition. Motion may be started by an earthquake, by excessive saturation of slope debris following a heavy rain or a time of melting snow and ice, by frost action, animal activity or blasting. Elsewhere, wherever a slope of loose debris and soil has been undercut, as along the seacoast, on a riverbank or in a roadcut, there may be extensive slumping.

On gentle slopes of soil and loose debris the downward motion of the land is less obvious. However, once attention is called to certain features even this motion becomes clear. Telegraph poles and fence posts set on a slope may, after a number of years, be tilted downhill because of the relatively more rapid motion of the near surface soil material than that underneath. For this reason a tree growing on a moving slope shows a bent trunk. After the tree is tilted new growth will be straight up and if there is a more or less continuous slippage of the soil a tree under such conditions will lean downhill in its lower part and be progressively straighter higher up.

Where frost action is prominent creep may be very rapid. On freezing, rock and mineral particles in a water-soaked mass of soil are pushed out at right angles to the slope, because expansion is easiest in this direction. When the ground melts the particles will settle back vertically under the force of gravity. Thus after a freeze-and-thaw sequence any particles on a slope will be slightly further downhill than before. Heating and cooling, and wetting and drying cycles have the same but less noticeable effects on the movement of surface materials straight out away from the surface with contraction in a vertical direction. The repetition of any of these cycles for many years has the inevitable result of decreasing any declivity. On forested slopes the mat of roots tends to slow up the creep of the larger particles especially, but clay and fine silt may move quite readily through the root network. Furthermore, every time a tree on a hillside is blown over, its roots will tear up the soil, which will settle back further down the slope than its original position.

The universal presence of cracks or joints, never more than a few feet apart in all rocks, makes possible the easy deep entry of oxygen, water, and carbon dioxide, which react here as well as on the surface to form new compounds with the consequent destruction of the original solid rock. Joints, providing as they do planes of easy breakage and easy access to weathering agents, will always control the shape of weathered cliffs and ledges of rock. Sometimes the control may be very obvious, as in Franconia Notch, New Hampshire, where a group of intersecting fractures has fortuitously given part of the cliff face the shape of a man's profile when viewed from the proper angle. This scenic attraction, The Old Man of the Mountain, is no more than a geologically transitory feature which is in constant danger of crumbling away. Volcanic rocks often possess a columnar type of joint system, and such rocks on weathering will show a beautiful group of columns, such as those so well developed, for example, at Devil's Tower in Wyoming, and the Devil's Postpile in California.

The detailed sculpturing of the land anywhere is fine and delicate and emphasizes minute differences in rock resistance to weathering. Rock ledges are never smooth but have a corrugated appearance where the more resistant parts, such as patches of quartz, will stand out as small ridges and the weaker material will have crumbled away. Such differential weathering is apparent everywhere, and in the analysis of topographic landforms it is important to realize that the development of every landscape involves a balance between the processes of weathering and erosion and the resistances of various rock masses to this combined action. That is, topographic variations on all scales from major cliffs and canyons to miscroscopic irregularities inevitably reflect rock and structure variations.

At Bryce Canyon in Utah, pinnacled spirelike remnants are the most obvious features of the landscape. A series of horizontal limy shales and sands are here cut by vertical joints, which form planes of weakness which dominantly control the rock breakup. This verticality of weathering exists because the layers have more or less the same resistance to change, and thus have less control over the location and speed of weathering than do the joints. Slight differences in resistance to weathering do occur, however, between one bed and another, and lead to a thinning of the spires where the layers are weaker and a widening of the pinnacles where they are stronger. In striking contrast to this area, weathering at the Grand Canyon has been obviously controlled by the bedding. The rock layers vary a great deal in their resistance and thus a horizontally controlled landscape is evident, consisting of alternating cliffs and slopes. The shale layers form the slopes and the cliffs occur where sandstone or limestone outcrop. Here, however, joints do play an obvious secondary role and control to some extent the shape of the cliffs, by producing sharp-pointed re-entrants and buttresses.

The production of soil is closely associated with weathering. Plant and animal residues as well as living plants and animals, and disintegrated and decomposed mineral and rock fragments are all components of any soil. It is possible to recognize three layers in a typical soil. The outermost, topsoil, contains much organic material and is a zone from which there has been leaching or removal of the most soluble constituents. Underlying this is a zone where material carried down from above has been precipitated. This layer in turn overlies a zone of weathered parent rock. In the case of residual soils or those developed *in situ,* this bottom layer rests on solid bedrock, its unweathered precursor. Where the soil is one which has been transported by the wind, rivers, or the glaciers, the parent mineral and rock fragments at the base of the soil profile are of course unlike the bedrock of the area. The formation of a soil may be relatively rapid. The extensive ash fall accompanying the 1883 eruption of the volcano Krakatoa shows significant chemical changes in the surface layers, and in places a well-developed soil profile has formed in the short length of time since the ash accumulated.

In all soils there is a constant redistribution of materials, as a result of the movement of groundwater, and the activities of soil organisms both plant and animal. Under normal conditions, as erosion removes the top layers, soil-building processes develop the lower layers. Under certain artificial conditions, however, such as the loss of all plant cover, the rate of removal is greatly increased and the soil is not replaced as fast as it is removed. In this way much soil in the United States has been ruined because the natural rate of erosion has been dramatically increased.

The weathering of any mass of rock and the removal of the broken fragments of course result in the general lowering of the surface of the land. And if in this process certain minerals and elements are taken away faster than others there will be a concentration at the surface of those which have been removed at the slowest rate. Flint nodules concentrate at the surface of a chalk terrain because they are far less soluble than the surrounding chalk in which they appeared initially as widely separated concretionary masses. In places, especially in warm humid areas, residual soils may be so rich in iron or aluminum that they form a minable source for these metals, a laterite soil. In such cases the aluminum occurs in the mineral bauxite, a hydrous aluminum compound, and iron as hydrous iron oxide. In the Amazon Basin the laterite soil has been found to be as much as 70 feet deep. The lushness of the vegetation here in such humid areas belies the essential poverty of the soil, where most of the organic material is broken down by the luxuriant abundance of bacteria, insects, worms, and various other organisms.

The presence of any rock ledge at the surface of the earth generally indicates extensive weathering and erosion, because essentially all hard rocks, with the exception of lava flows, are made at depth. The consolidation of sediments into sedimentary rock takes place under the surface, metamorphic rocks are formed there, and many igneous rocks solidify there, where pressures and temperatures are much higher than those at the earth's surface. Weathering is the inevitable adjustment of rocks formed at depth to this new enviroment of the earth's surface.

(*Union Pacific Railroad*)

Geyser in Yellowstone Park, Wyoming

CHAPTER VI

UNDERGROUND WATER

The water of the world is in constant motion. Evaporated from the seas it is carried over the land to fall as rain or snow, and then it may flow off on the surface, sink underground, or be re-evaporated. This water cycle starts with the ultimate reservoir, the sea, and includes the vapor stage in the air, and the liquid and ice stages on and under the land. Water has constantly shifted between these various environments, and the average water molecule has probably been in each unmeasured times during earth history.

It has been estimated that approximately 30 inches of rain falls on the United States every year. This precipitation, however, is very far from uniform both in space and in time; some areas of the country are deserts and some well watered with a copious supply. The equivalent of 21 inches out of the 30 return directly to the atmosphere by evaporation or by transpiration, that is, evaporation from vegetation. This leaves nine inches to flow back to the sea, and most of it makes at least part of its journey underground.

The volume of groundwater at any one time in the upper half-mile of the crust of the earth is over 3,000 times greater than the volume of water in all the rivers, and nearly 20 times as much as that in all the rivers and lakes, both fresh and salt combined. The underground supply is thus extremely important as an equalizer for stream flow. Perennial streams continue to flow because they are fed from underground sources, by springs and water seeping out at the surface. If all the groundwater in North America were brought to the surface it would cover the land to a depth of somewhat over 100 inches, the equivalent of several times the annual precipitation.

DISTRIBUTION OF THE WORLD'S WATER SUPPLY

Location	Volume (Cubic miles)
Surface water	
Fresh lakes	30,000
Salt lakes	25,000
In stream channels	300
Underground water	
Less than ½ mile deep	1,000,000
Over ½ mile deep	1,000,000
Glaciers	7,000,000
Atmosphere	3,000
Oceans	317,000,000
Total world's water	326,000,000
	(to nearest 1,000,000)

Source: R. L. Nace.

The presence and motion of water depends on the universal occurrence of small spaces below the surface, such as interstices between sand grains and soil particles, cracks in jointed rock and still larger passageways in dissolved limestone, and porous lava flows. The amount of water in any mass of rock underground is dependent on the porosity of the rock, that is, the percentage of openings present. Where openings are connected one with another, rainwater will readily percolate into the ground to reappear eventually as springs at a lower elevation at the bottom or sides of valleys. Inasmuch as most underground openings are small and tortuously connected, the motion of water through them is extremely slow. In highly permeable materials, that is, materials where openings are large and well connected, motion may be relatively rapid, perhaps 10 to 20 feet a day. Where openings are smaller and less well connected, motions of 50 to 100 feet per year may be typical. Compared with surface streams, the flow of water under the surface is very slow indeed. It may stay underground from a few hours to many years, and in the deeper parts of the crust it is essentially stagnant, remaining in the same place perhaps for thousands of years.

The distribution of water underground is very far from uniform. Probably less than 10 per cent of the rocks in the upper part of the crust are of the type to yield water readily if wells are sunk into

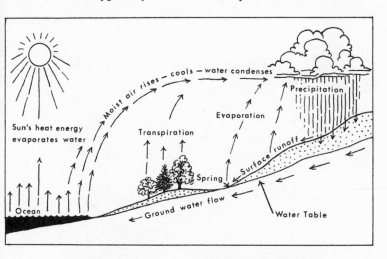

Diagrammatic representation of the water cycle

them, that is, are both porous and permeable. Gravel, sand, sandstone, porous basalt, fractured and dissolved limestone, and in general any well-jointed and fissured solid rock, have plenty of pore spaces, and generally the openings are connected so that as rapidly as water is pumped from a well sunk in such rocks more water will flow from the surroundings into the well opening. Groundwater is present and moves only through the upper few thousands of feet of the crust, generally less than a mile. The rock pressure below a few miles is such that openings do not develop.

Water-bearing rocks, or aquifers, are found in a number of locations. Glacial deposits of sand and gravel, alluvial fan, floodplain, and delta deposits of sand all provide excellent water sources, and as noted, consolidated rocks, if well jointed, will supply water.

When a well penetrates a saturated mass of coarse gravel or

sand, it may appear that it has hit an underground river, but the use of the term "river" here conveys a false picture of the true situation, because water is not flowing along an open channel. Only in the case of flow through limestone caverns and tunnels dissolved in soluble rocks should we speak of underground rivers as being similar to surface streams.

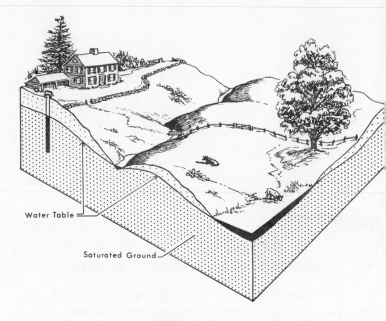

The water table

In general any hole drilled into the earth will initially penetrate material whose pore spaces are not full of water, before reaching a level below which all openings are filled. The water table is this underground surface which separates a water-saturated zone from overlying rocks and soil where the openings are only partly filled, the zone of aeration.

The water table varies from a few feet below the surface of the ground to many feet, especially in arid areas where it may lie at depths of hundreds of feet. In general it is a subdued replica of the ground surface and can be visualized as a hill of water looping up under the topographic hills. Perennial lakes, marshes, and streams mark areas where the water table has emerged and lies above the surface of the ground. If the rocks below such waterlogged areas were not themselves saturated with as much water as they could hold, the surface water would disappear underground. The location of the water table elsewhere is shown by the water level in wells. In the zone of aeration there is generally some absorbed water, and water in capillary-sized openings, but there are still openings to be filled by rainwater percolating down from above. Obviously, after a heavy rain the water table will rise, and after a time of drought it will sink, the rate of sinking depending on the permeability of the rocks.

Springs are points of surface discharge where the water table intersects the ground surface. Perennial streams lie essentially in troughs in the saturated part of the ground, where water generally is emerging at the surface. Intermittent streams, those flowing only at times of rain, lie above the water table for most of the time, and water flowing in them will quickly disappear, some of it underground to raise the level of the water table, and some of it by evaporation.

The effect of man on the level of the water table can be locally very important. Perhaps the most significant effect follows the large-scale removal of water from wells. A well from which water is being pumped has much the same effect on the water table as a perennial stream valley. In both, water flows from the saturated ground into an opening. Water which is pumped from any well is replaced by more from neighboring saturated ground in just the same way that a perennial stream is kept flowing by being fed by groundwater. The net result of either action is to lower the water table in the nearby area. In a number of arid and semiarid regions the water table has been artifically lowered many tens of feet. This is bound to happen wherever water is taken out from underground faster than it is being replaced by rainfall.

The percentage of rainwater which soaks into the ground before flowing off on the surface depends on the rapidity of runoff as well as on soil permeability. Deforestation will speed up the runoff and thus lessen the amount returning to the ground. Irrigation projects and the building of reservoirs will, on the other hand, increase the amount of percolation back underground. The construction of impermeable surfaces such as sidewalks and paved streets in cities acts in a manner similar to deforestation, and leads to increase in the rate of runoff and a decrease in the return underground.

A number of problems have arisen following man's removal of groundwater and the consequent lowering of the water table. If water is taken out of the ground near the ocean, salt water may intrude to replace it, and thus fresh-water aquifers may become salty. This type of trouble has occurred at a number of places, such as Brooklyn, New York; Baltimore; Galveston; and Long Beach, California. Furthermore, there may be some subsidence of the land if a great deal of ground water is removed. This has happened in the Central Valley of California, and in Mexico City.

Groundwater passing through the crust to an eventual reappearance may traverse rocks whose temperature is much higher than that at the surface and it will then emerge as hot springs. The increase of the temperature with depth is universal but varies greatly from place to place, being understandably greatest in volcanically active regions. Hot springs are often associated with a fault, which intersects hot rock at depth, and along which a convective system develops. At Warm Springs, Georgia, surface water goes to a depth of about 3,800 feet, is heated, and then re-emerges at a temperature of about 88 degrees F. Here the normal rock temperature increases about 1 degree F per 100-foot depth.

Periodically eruptive hot springs, or geysers, are notable in three widely separated places—Iceland, Yellowstone Park, and New Zealand. In Yellowstone Park there are about 100 such features, in Iceland about 30 true geysers and in New Zealand somewhat fewer.

The classic theory of geyser action was proposed by Bunson in 1846, and is based on the fact that pressure increases the boiling point of water, and that the greater the pressure the higher the temperature must be before this point can be reached. At sea level under the pressure of one atmosphere, water boils at 212 degrees F, and at two atmospheres, which is reached in the earth under a water depth of 33 feet, the boiling point is 248 degrees F. At a depth of 787 feet, equivalent to a pressure of 25 atmospheres, water boils at a temperature of 437 degrees F. Thus water at the bottom of a deep crack must be heated well above the surface boiling point before it is transformed into steam. The assumption is made that in a tortuous crack filled with water, convection will not occur to allow the hotter water at depth to rise to the surface. If there is sufficient heat, however, the water at depth will eventually be turned into steam. This superheated steam can then rise through the crack and as it does so will cause water at the higher levels to change into vapor until eventually the whole column will be a mass of steam and water which will emerge explosively at the surface. The crack thus blown essentially free of water will be filled again with cool groundwater and a time interval must elapse before the whole process is repeated.

Hot springs in various parts of the world have long been used as sources of heat. Recently holes have been drilled in the ground to tap superheated steam to produce geothermal power. Such power is available in areas where the normal geothermal gradient is greatly increased by the near-surface approach of magma. There are four areas which have recently been exploited seriously for power: northern Italy, New Zealand, Iceland, and California.

The Larderello area of Italy, about 40 miles from Florence, lies at the northern end of a volcanic belt which includes Vesuvius. Here natural steam vents have been known for centuries. The rocks were first drilled for steam in 1904, and now over 300,000 kilowatts of energy is developed. The temperature of the steam varies between 266 and 440 degrees F, with pressures from 71 to 390 pounds per square inch. The magmatic source of the steam is indicated by the abundance of boric acid as well as a number of other compounds associated with magmas. The source of the water is considered by many to be a granite magma. When granite freezes from a liquid state it will release approximately 6 per cent by weight of water and the freezing of about 5½ cubic miles of granite magma would have supplied the Larderello steam vents for 700 years at the natural rate of production.

The Geysers area of California 95 miles north of San Francisco began to be developed for steam power in the late 1950s. The name is a misnomer, since there are no real geysers here but a number of hot springs. The steam that was tapped at depth is considered to be mostly of magmatic origin because it is superheated, and accompanied by various gases commonly associated with volcanic eruptions. Also there is a very meager supply of groundwater in this generally dry area, apparently far too small to supply the quantities emitted from the hot springs.

Erosion by groundwater is most obvious in limestone areas where caves, sinkholes, and disappearing streams may be common. Limestone, calcium carbonate, is essentially insoluble in pure water but rapidly dissolves in rainwater which contains some carbonic acid, the combination of water and carbon dioxide. Thus wherever limestone is encountered in the journey of water back to the sea it is liable to be dissolved.

Limestone caves are fashioned under some conditions of groundwater circulation and at other times deposits of dripstone occur, partially filling them. The fantastic display of cave deposits is based on variations of three basic shapes, consisting of stalactites, the iciclelike pendants from the ceiling, stalagmites or stumpy growths from the floor, and pillars. The variety in shape and color which makes each cave deposit unique is due to the interplay of a number of factors such as slight variations in the arrangement of cracks down which groundwater percolates, the rate of water flowage, the temperature, the chemistry of the solutions, and the rate of deposition.

Carlsbad in New Mexico is one of the largest limestone cave systems in the United States. One gallery, the Big Room, is 4,000 feet long, with a maximum width of 625 feet and a maximum ceiling height of 300 feet. Other noted caves are Mammoth, Kentucky; Luray, Virginia; Wyondotte and Marengo in Indiana; and Wind Cave in South Dakota.

Sinkholes are the commonest and most widespread erosional features found in limestone regions. They are depressions which vary in depth from just a few feet to 100 feet or more, and in area from a few square yards to a number of acres. In places they are isolated, but most commonly they occur in swarms, one right next to another, so that there may be hundreds in a square mile. The sides of the hollows are steep and it is very difficult to cross a well-developed sinkhole area. Sinks result from the enlargement of solution channels along upright joints, or from the collapse of weakened roofs over a part of an underground passageway.

The formation of a natural bridge, such as that in Virginia, by contrast with a sinkhole, is a very rare event in limestone areas. The Virginia example is a roof remnant left when an underground river channel, enlarged by solution, was exposed to view, following the collapse of all but a narrow part of the rock which once covered it. The top of the bridge is now 150 feet above the exposed stream, and varies in width from 50 to 150 feet throughout its 100-foot length.

Caves, sinkholes, solution valleys, natural bridges, and a network of many short gullies and ravines terminating abruptly where water goes underground all may characterize a limestone terrain which has been exposed to groundwater erosion. Surface streams are absent as most of the drainage will be via underground passageways. The type locality for this landscape is the Karst area in Yugoslavia. Karst topography develops best in well-jointed, moderately thick limestone layers. The joints concentrate the flow and thus the solution activity of the percolating water. Rainfall should be moderately heavy, and there must be a major stream at a lower elevation than the general level of the area which will enable the groundwater to drain away easily. If the limestone is essentially horizontal it will outcrop over an extensive area, and a widespread Karst region will be formed. Well-known sinkhole areas with many other Karst features are found in the United States in central Florida, southern Indiana, and parts of central Kentucky and Tennessee.

Chalk, in comparison with the harder and more massive varieties of limestone, is permeable throughout its mass rather than just along the joints, and thus is not dissolved significantly more in one place than in another. Therefore, in chalk areas sinkholes and caves are few and not well developed. However clear the water of a stream may appear, there is always some dissolved material in it, and rivers draining a limestone area may carry a very significant load of calcium carbonate in solution. Spring water is apt to contain a still greater percentage of dissolved mineral matter, and hot springs the most. When hot springs emerge at the surface the dissolved load is deposited as a result of a number of factors, such as the loss of carbon dioxide, evaporation, release of pressure, or a drop in temperature. Calcium carbonate, as tufa and travertine, forms probably the most abundant spring deposits, and often occurs in the form of terraces, such as at Mammoth Hot Springs, in Yellowstone Park. Silica, SiO_2, is deposited as the mineral geyserite, or silicious sinter, around many geysers in Yellowstone Park.

The deposition underground of calcite, silica, or iron oxide is especially important in the process of rock consolidation. Such cements, picked up in one environment by groundwater, may be deposited elsewhere to join together sedimentary particles of silt, sand, and gravel.

Occasionally a local concentration of one of the natural cements will result in the formation of a concretion. These vary in size from a fraction of an inch to several feet across, and are commonly spheroidal or discoidal in shape, and occur where a sedimentary bed is more firmly cemented at one place than another. Silica in the form of chert or flint is often found as nodular masses in chalk and limestone. These are knobby-shaped bodies which grow as the original calcium carbonate is replaced. Elsewhere groundwater may perform a very delicate job of replacement when it deposits silica and removes woody fibers at the same time. Frequently the replacement is so delicate that the original growth rings in the wood are preserved in all their intricate detail. In the Petrified Forest National Monument in Arizona a stone forest is now being exposed to view. Many tree trunks and stone chips which resemble wood piles stand out clearly against the soft colorful shale of the Painted Desert. The forest which once flourished here was buried under sand and mud, and the wood changed to stone. Then, times of deposition changed to times of erosion and the forest was uncovered, giving us today's landscape.

Economically useful mineral concentrations may be produced by groundwater. Original deposits of some ore minerals found in veins or widely disseminated as isolated masses through a rock may be weathered along with the host rock and certain elements dissolved and transferred in solution to a lower level where they are redeposited, often in the form of a new mineral. Important deposits of copper in an enriched form have this origin. For example, at Bisbee, Arizona, deposits enriched by groundwater circulation have yielded over 2½ million tons of copper and large amounts of silver.

CHAPTER VII

RIVERS

Running water is unquestionably the most powerful and important of all the agents of erosion. Rainwash, sheets of water flooding down slopes, swirling, eddying and rushing streams all result from gravity pulling water downhill toward the sea. A stream is constantly modifying the terrain over which it flows, sometimes dramatically when flood waters undercut riverbanks, wash out roads, and cut new channels for themselves, and at other times slowly and almost imperceptibly. Even in many desert areas where rains are rare, the most obvious erosional features are water-worn gullies and rain-washed slopes, the work of occasional flash floods.

The energy available from running and falling water is tremendous, and comes from the yearly return to the sea of approximately 8,400 cubic miles of water as it drops off the land from an average elevation of 2,700 feet. The Amazon River, the world's largest, empties into the ocean about 1,600 cubic miles of water per year. This flow is approximately 12 times the total for the Mississippi River, and five times the flow of the Congo, the world's second largest river. The total yearly runoff from continental United States is about 390 cubic miles, and at the present time, the country uses on the whole somewhat over 100 cubic miles for irrigation, industry, and water use in general. It comes both from rivers and from underground, and of course, most of it after use is returned to its original environment, often however, in a polluted condition.

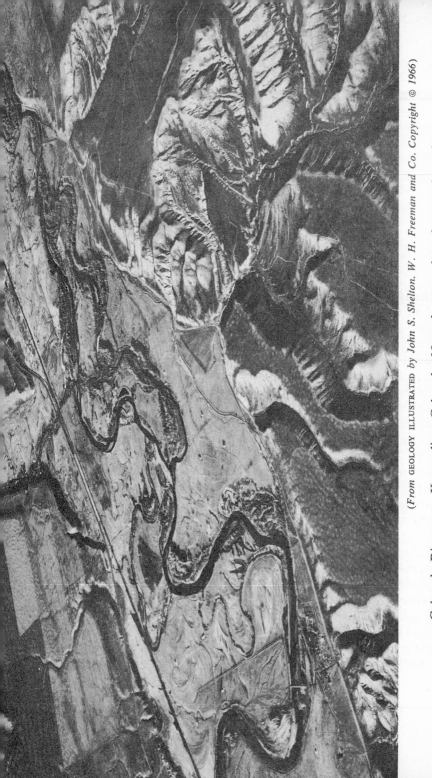

(*From* GEOLOGY ILLUSTRATED *by John S. Shelton. W. H. Freeman and Co. Copyright © 1966*)

Colorado River near Kremmling, Colorado. Note the meanders, former channels,

At any one time there are about 300 cubic miles of water in all the river channels of the world, which is enough for 13 days' flow at the average rate of 23 cubic miles a day. Obviously this flow is maintained directly by added rainfall, plus a large and significant fraction coming from underground.

Rivers transport material in three ways. Some materials are carried in solution, some in suspension, and larger particles, gravel, and boulders, are rolled and pushed down the streambed. The proportion of the load in solution to that in suspension varies greatly depending upon the location of the river. In arid and semi-arid regions the dissolved load is a relatively small part of the total, whereas in humid, vegetation-covered areas, it is a much larger part. In such latter areas the load carried in suspension and along the bottom is relatively small, because vegetation slows up the removal of debris from the land, except in the dissolved state. For instance, approximately 1 per cent of the load of the Little Colorado River is in solution, 45 per cent of the load of the Delaware River past Trenton, and 64 per cent of the load of the Juniata River near Newport, Pennsylvania. The solution and suspension loads collectively account for the great bulk of the material transported by any stream. That moved by rolling and sliding along the bottom averages about 10 per cent of the suspended load, except in mountain areas where the bed load of streams with very steep gradients may be a number of times the suspended load, and be carried essentially only at times of flood.

At times of high water, streams which flow on sand and gravel, such as the Mississippi and Missouri rivers, scour up their channels and increase their load in suspension. The depth of scour in such a channel may be as much as ½ the increase of the elevation of the water surface at flood times.

The general recognition that springs and rivers are fed ultimately from rainfall has been accepted for only the last 300 years or so. From classical times through the Renaissance various other ideas for their origin were given. Most of the theories proposed that seawater in some fashion entered the earth and reappeared in mountain areas to flow back to the ocean. Some authors admitted that perhaps some of the water was from precipitation, but apparently no one was willing to postulate that all springs and rivers were fed from this source only. Various suggestions were made as to the ways in which seawater could reach the mountaintops. One proposal called on the evaporation of seawater by internal fires of the earth, and the condensation of the resulting vapor as it rose via underground passageways into the snowy and cold mountain areas. Another theory called attention to the curvature of the earth and held that ocean waters were actually higher than the land. The enormous weight of the ocean waters, especially at times of high tides, were thought by some people to be capable of forcing water up through cracks in the crust to the tops of the mountains. Other proposals were based on the supposed attraction of the land for water, which was thought to be pulled up through cracks, or on the influence of the heavens, which attracted water in some such manner as a magnet attracts iron. Note that in all these explanations the suggested methods of water transfer from ocean levels upward took place underground. The water after this subterranean journey appeared in springs and then flowed back to the sea on the surface.

The first actual measurements to show that precipitation was adequate to supply more than enough water for all the springs and rivers in an area was made by Pierre Perrault, who in 1674 published *L'Origine des Fontaines* in which he gave the results of his measurements of rainfall in a small part of the drainage area of the Seine River, and compared this with the flow of the streams in the area. He found that the river flow accounted for only about $\frac{1}{6}$ of the rainfall. A few years later M. Mariotte measured a somewhat larger area of the Seine drainage, and on comparing it with the river flow found that the river carried about $\frac{1}{8}$ of the precipitation. Since then there has been no doubt that precipitation is the ultimate source of all ground and stream water, and that stream flow is but one part of the water cycle, in which seawater is evaporated, the vapor carried over the land to be changed to rain or snow which then returns to the ocean as rivers of water or of ice, with generally part of the journey via underground passages.

The valley is the basic erosional form produced by the action of water as it flows back to the sea. It may vary in size from the smallest crease indenting a hillside to the major canyons of the world. The complementary production of hills and divides between neighboring valleys is intimately associated with valley carving, such features being residual in origin and appearing only as the valleys are cut.

Many years ago it was generally believed that valleys resulted from catastrophic events in nature, that the land had split open and thus formed these cracks down which water flowed back to the sea. It was not until 1802, when John Playfair in a classic statement neatly stated the proposition that rivers do cut their own valleys, that this new idea concerning the origin for valleys began to be generally accepted. His argument was based on the observation that streams and their tributaries as a rule have accordant junctions, that is, however far away a tributary may start and however devious its course, its valley has the proper slope so that when it reaches the main river valley its waters can merge with those of the principal stream at the same elevation. That this situation might be true in the case of a few valleys of cataclysmic origin is conceivable, but that it should be true for all the tributaries and subtributaries of a river system is not possible. On the other hand, if rivers cut their own valleys, and tributaries are developed in general after the main valley, such accordant junctions are expectable, and any deviation therefrom is cause for a special explanation.

The major aspects of a river valley are the channel, in which the water flows, and the walls extending above the present reach of the stream. The actual channel, that is, the small cut filled with water at the bottom of the valley, is a self-formed and self-maintained feature. Water has carved the groove, adjusting the depth and cross-sectional configuration to conform with the material which it carries and the amount of water which is fed to it by rain, springs and tributaries combined. Any existing stream channel is inherited from an earlier one, and has evolved through time, adapting itself to changing conditions of climate. It has been calculated that there are probably over 3 million miles of such channels in the United States, including all the minor creeks, many of which have water flowing in them only during a time of rain.

The actual formation of any river valley has two aspects, deepening and widening. Water flowing down any initial slope is concentrated in the lower parts and forms a groove in the land. Such a groove is eventually cut deep enough so that for most of the time water flows at the bottom only, and walls of rock or soil extend above the general stream level. Material on these slopes is weathered, and slips and slides down to the channel to be washed away by the stream which uses this debris as a tool to cut its channel still deeper. This process exposes more valley walls and the procedure is continued indefinitely until the river has increased the depth of its channel and thus has decreased its gradient to such an extent that it no longer cuts downward. Thus, the average winding stream-cut valley with water flowing at the bottom and with flaring sides reaching upward, has been deepened by the river abrading a path for itself, and widened, above the reach of the present water, by weathering and mass-wasting. Rain wash and the cutting of gullied tributaries to the principal valley also aid in valley widening. The flaring sides of any typical youthful valley become farther and farther apart as one goes up the valley side, because the higher parts of the walls have been exposed longer to the destructive forces of the weather; furthermore, they may collapse by undercutting of the stream from underneath.

The V-shaped transverse profile of a youthful stream valley, whatever its modification, gentle, steep, asymmetric or stepped, is present as long as a stream has enough carrying capacity to remove all debris brought to it either directly as slide material from the valley walls or by tributaries. Falls and rapids are expectable as long as a river is cutting downward and the V-shaped valley prevails. Rock is never of uniform resistance for any great distance, and wherever a river flowing across the land moves from an area of more resistant rock to one of less resistance, there will be falls or rapids. The river with its load of abrasive sand and gravel particles cuts the softer rocks away more rapidly, thus leaving the harder material at a higher elevation.

Niagara Falls is a classic example of a waterfall resulting when a river flows from a resistant layer onto weaker ones. In this case the resistant layer is a limestone which is slightly tilted upstream. The river flows across the uptilted edge onto lower and weaker materials. The falls are held up by this resistant layer or cap rock, and the swirling, eddying action underneath the falls cuts and abrades the softer material away both downward to form a plunge pool and backward under the falls. Eventually a cave may be formed here and if this becomes deep enough a bit of the cap rock breaks off and the falls are said to have retreated. The seven-mile-long Niagara Gorge, extending downstream from the present falls, was formed in just this fashion by the retreat of the falls during the last 20,000 to 25,000 years. At the present time approximately 95 per cent of the water in the Niagara River goes over the Horseshoe Falls on the Canadian side, with the result that the falls here are

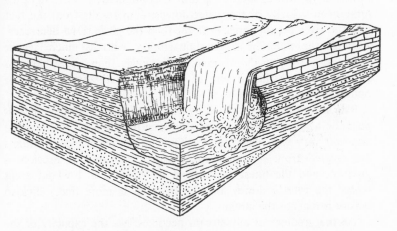

Idealized section of Niagara Falls. Note the cap rock of limestone, which is being undercut by river action.

retreating far more rapidly than those on the American side. The Canadian falls drop 158 feet into a plunge pool 192 feet deep. There is no plunge pool under the American falls but there is a pile of debris in process of being broken up and carried away.

The series of falls and rapids developed on each of the numerous rivers coming from the west which cross the boundary between the hard rocks of the Piedmont and the softer rocks of the Atlantic Coastal Plain mark the fall zone. Here the rivers such as the Potomac River at Washington, D.C., find themselves shifting from hard rock onto softer, with again the result that falls and rapids are produced at this junction, and hence the term "Fall Zone" for this dividing line.

The erosive action of swirling, gyrating water as it carries sand

and gravel across any streambed may produce rounded, smooth-sided hollows, or potholes, in the rocky floor of the channel. These are similar in origin to the much larger plunge pools at the base of many waterfalls.

As one follows any typical floodplain river downstream, it is found that the width of the river, the depth of the water and, strangely, the velocity also, increase. The added volume of water from the various tributaries is thus accommodated. The slight alteration in velocity of the water downstream results from the fact that the river depth increases faster than the river slope decreases. Actually the water in a mountain stream, with its much steeper gradient, moves, on the average, more slowly than one is likely to imagine because the amount of eddying and the friction on the bouldery bed is very great.

The size of material carried by a stream varies from the coarsest near the headwaters to a finer load along the channel. Further, the size will vary with the rate of erosion. The coarsest constitutents are carried from mountain areas where the rate of erosion is greatest, and the finest are carried by streams in lowland areas where the rate is slower and the material is more finely divided before it reaches the stream.

As the gradient of any stream becomes less the capacity of the river to move material will eventually dwindle, and in time will just equal the load of debris brought to the main channel by all the tributaries. A stream at this stage is considered to be a mature stream; it has stopped down-cutting and starts to meander across its own floodplain, on deposits composed of debris which it is in the process of slowly moving seaward. The characteristic change is very clearcut between a youthful stream with its V-shaped cross-profile, flowing on bedrock, and often with falls and rapids, and the mature stream with a flat floor, a meandering course, and no falls or rapids. Any youthful stream must of necessity, after it has cut down close enough to sea level, lose its youthful characteristics and become mature. It is inevitable that this should be so. However, this conclusion can be put off more or less indefinitely if the land is constantly rising with respect to sea level, the ultimate level to which all land erosion is working. The river then will continually have to cut down and ever down. The Colorado, for instance, has been flowing for millions of years through the Grand Canyon area, and yet it is still a youthful river, it still flows on bedrock at the bottom of the Canyon, and a roughly V-shaped profile is present, the steplike walls rising directly from the river channel to the Canyon rim.

In general, the longer a stream has been mature the wider the floodplain will be, and the greater the distance between the bluffs at the sides of the valley. At times of flood such a stream overflows its banks and water may cover the floodplain. Fine material in suspension will be carried widely to settle slowly wherever the floodwaters reach. The coarser material is likely to be deposited close to the meandering channel, where the velocity of the flood-water is first checked. These deposits build up natural levees or sinuous ridgelike features which closely parallel the principal channel on either side.

The location of the loops of a meandering stream are forever shifting, outward and slightly downstream, because the river undercuts the outside of its banks as it turns a bend and builds up deposits on the inside of the bend, where the water is moving less rapidly. A sequence of these crescent-shaped point bar deposits, laid down on the inside of the bend of a shifting meander loop, are often very noticeable from the air, and form intricate patterns when many loops of a river are viewed at one time.

At times the position of the channel may change still more rapidly. For instance, during a flood, a meander loop may be abandoned by the river as it takes a new and shorter course. This leaves a crescent-shaped part of the former channel behind, form-ing a so-called ox-bow lake. Old maps of the Mississippi River show marked shifts of the location of the meanders, both by the cutting off of loops and by the slower shifting of the sinuous chan-nel itself. Early property boundaries frequently followed the river, and thus the shifting channel has through the years led to much controversy.

The clear distinction between the characteristics of youthful and mature streams are obvious in the field and on a map. Distinctions between a mature and a possible old-age stage are less obvious and are arbitrary. Some geologists define the old-age stage of a stream as being attained when the width of the floodplain valley is a specified number of times the width of the meander belt. It seems more realistic, however, to recognize only two major ages in the growth of a stream, the youthful and the mature or floodplain stages. The longer the floodplain river exists the wider in general will be the plain over which it meanders in comparison with the average width of the meander belt.

Floodplain rivers with their meanders may become rejuvenated because of an increased flow of water or a decreased load, following a change in climate, or because of a rise in velocity caused by an uplift of the land. They will start to cut down as they did in their youthful days. The stream will thus entrench itself in its own floodplain deposits, remnants of which may be left as flat terraces at the sides of the new lower river. A number of times of rejuvenation will result in the production of a number of terraces one above the other. Such levels are a common feature along many rivers and can be identified by their layers of sand and gravel when newly exposed in a roadcut. Particularly fine examples of such terraces are to be found along the Madison River in Montana.

Following extensive uplift a meandering stream may remove all traces of its former floodplain and be found incising itself, as a youthful stream, into the underlying bedrock. Given sufficient time, these meanders may be incised thousands of feet deep. The Goosenecks of the San Juan River in southern Utah strongly suggest that at one time this river meandered freely across a floodplain.

A stream will dump its load whenever the rate of flow becomes less or the water disappears, either by evaporation or by sinking into the ground. At times of slack water any river will deposit sandbars which during flood will be shifted as the sand is moved still further along the channel. The location and the shape of such bars constantly change as the river level rises and falls in its seasonal cycles. This was the problem which faced the Mississippi River pilots in the days when the paddlewheel steamers were navigating the treacherous channels.

Alluvial fans are characteristic of arid to semiarid areas. They form where streams carrying material down from the mountains lose their velocity at the base of a slope and thus dump their load. They are land deposits with an origin very similar to that of deltas, which are built into bodies of standing water. Very striking examples of large alluvial fans are to be found in the Basin and Range Province of the western United States; here they have frequently coalesced to form vast, gentle slopes.

Much of the finest material of many streams which is in suspension is not deposited even briefly until it reaches a lake or the sea, where it will form a delta. The Mississippi River has constructed the best-known delta in America. Here the land has been built out many miles by river deposits, and the delta continues underwater for many more miles. The Continental Shelf, which is 80 to 100 miles wide in this area, has been virtually cut into two parts by these deposits, and the river is now supplying much sediment to the Continental Slope well beyond the present coastline, and has contributed to large underwater fans which extend some hundreds of miles from shore.

A number of deposits of economic importance are closely associated with riverbeds. Placer gold, diamonds, and tin have been concentrated in stream channels in a number of places in the world. Such materials are comparatively indestructible at the earth's surface and are relatively heavy so that they tend to settle to the bottom of sand and gravel layers, as these are built up by stream action. A classic area of placer gold is in the Central Valley of California, at the foot of the Sierra Nevada Mountains. Weathering has loosened gold particles along with quartz and other minerals from veins in the mountains at the east. This debris was then washed by streams down into the Central Valley, where gold is now found concentrated in the lower parts of the irregular stream channels and in various outwash and fan deposits. Such placer gold is obviously of secondary origin. The primary gold occurring as veins in association with quartz was found and exploited somewhat after the placer gold had been discovered.

Given long enough, a group of streams, aided by mass-wasting, must inevitably destroy any land mass and produce a surface characterized by gentle slopes and drained by slow-moving streams. Above such an erosion surface of old age, called a peneplain if of large extent, there may be here and there residual remnants or monadnocks. These exist because they may be composed of slightly more resistant material, or they may lie in areas well away from any major stream, and thus have not been attacked as vigorously. At the present time in earth history there is no example of the ideal peneplain on the face of the earth. Apparently no extensive part of the land, in the recent geologic past, has been stable long enough for the attainment of this ultimate stage.

Mount Monadnock in southern New Hampshire, the type example, does not rise over a present-day peneplain, but over an erosion surface which was presumed to have existed some tens of millions of years ago. A visit to this area shows a rolling countryside, with streams in narrow valleys and rounded hills between the valleys. From the top of these lower hills one notices that they all reach essentially the same elevation and if, in imagination, the more recently formed valleys are filled in, a relatively flat surface results. This marks the erosion surface above which Mount Monadnock extends still higher. Thus the type example of a monadnock is a residual remnant rearing above a presumed peneplain which no longer exists as such, but has been destroyed by a new generation of stream valleys.

If the forces of erosion alone were active it has been estimated that any large part of the earth's surface would probably be eroded to a rolling surface near sea level in less than 100 million years. The present rate at which the United States as a whole is being lowered is about $2\frac{1}{2}$ inches every 1,000 years. This rate is far from uniform throughout the country. The Colorado River drainage basin, for instance, is being reduced in elevation at the relatively rapid rate of $6\frac{1}{2}$ inches every 1,000 years.

If the present rapid rate of general removal were maintained, all the country above sea level would be carried into the ocean in somewhat over 10 million years. However, present rates of denudation would certainly not be maintained as the general level of the land was lowered, and the ultimate reduction of the land to essentially sea level would take very much longer.

CHAPTER VIII

COASTLINES AND THE SEA

Seventy-one per cent of the earth's surface is covered by the oceans, and in comparison with the land little is yet known in detail of this part of the world. Exploring the sea floor has been likened to exploring the earth's continental surface from a balloon through a layer of clouds by means of soundings, and perhaps samples of surface rock and soil taken every few hundred miles.

The position of mean sea level varies from place to place and has varied throughout geologic time. The equatorial radius of the earth is about $13\frac{1}{3}$ miles longer than the polar radius, and thus the distance from the earth's center to sea level is larger by this much. It is slightly greater near mountainous coasts such as the Pacific Ocean side of South America where the gravitational pull of the Andes distorts the ocean level upward. Temporary variations due to tides, changes in air pressure, and winds affect sea level from place to place and time to time. Furthermore, it is lowered on a worldwide scale by downwarping of the sea floor in any of the ocean basins, and conversely is raised by delta-building or the piling up of sediments in the sea. Locally, changes between land and sea occur as the result of mountain-building, flexing of crustal layers both upward and downward, and by volcanic activity. The melting of the large ice sheets which formerly covered both Canada and Scandinavia has removed a load so that these areas have risen some hundreds of feet. Furthermore, during a time of major

(Oregon State Highway Commission)

Cliffs and sea stacks at Cape Sebastian, Oregon

glaciation, much water is locked up on the land in the form of ice, and thus a general lowering of sea level must result, while the melting of the ice causes a rise.

Another probable cause for sea-level variations is connected with changes in the rate of the earth's rotation. It has been calculated that this rate has slowed up owing to tidal friction by as much as $\frac{1}{50}$ since the Cretaceous. This should have the expected result of lowering sea level in the equatorial regions and raising it in the polar, because of the lessened centrifugal force connected with the slower rate of rotation. Assuming that the oceans responded immediately to such a change of force, but that the solid parts of the earth lagged behind, the lowering of sea level at the equator might have been as much as 600 feet, according to some geologists, and the rise at the poles an equivalent amount.

As a consequence of this ever shifting relationship between land and sea, the position of shoreline and thus the location of wave and current attack must also shift.

A visit to the coast gives one a glimpse of what has happened throughout the long reaches of the past, and will happen in the future. What characteristically occurs along any shore is taking place along all the shores of the world. Here the never ceasing action of the waves, tides, and currents constantly modifies the scenery, wearing away the land at one place and building it out elsewhere. It is along the shorelines that the instability of the earth's crust is perhaps most obvious, the transitory nature of the scenic elements most easily seen, and the changing relationship between land and sea most evident.

The sea destroys the land in a number of ways. The impact of water, laden with sand and gravel which act as cutting abrasive tools, is effective on both consolidated and unconsolidated material. An idea of the fantastic force of waves and their effective reach is given by such reports as that from Tillamook Rock Lighthouse on the Oregon coast where waves have repeatedly hurled stones large enough to break the heavy glass of the light 130 feet above sea level. The hydraulic action of water, that is, water moving directly, is really effective only against unconsolidated sands, gravels, and clays. However, in rare instances air may be trapped and compressed in a crack by the forward motion of a wave, and the resulting pressure may be adequate to shatter even solid rocks. Corrosion, the chemical weathering of salt water with its contained oxygen and carbon dioxide, is quite effective in places, especially on limestone. Obviously, such attack is much slower in its effect than that connected with the direct action of waves.

Waves vary in length from very small ripples a fraction of an inch long, with a fraction of a second elapsing between successive crests, to large waves in the open ocean, to earthquake waves or tsunamis with a wave length up to 100 miles and with 10 to 20 minutes between crests, to the tides themselves, with distances between crests being halfway around the world and a time between crests of slightly more than 12 hours.

The force which drives the oceans into waves, except for tsunamis and the tides, comes from the frictional drag of winds over the surface of the water. Winds in turn result essentially from the attempt of the atmosphere to return to equilibrium after being heated more in one place than in another. The gravitational pull of sun and moon gives the tides, and faulting on the ocean bottom, or other ocean-floor disturbances, produce tsunamis.

One of the most characteristic features of the coast is the wave-eroded sea cliff, which is of course most easily produced in soft material but is also found in hard resistant rocks. The production of such features has led in many places in the world to a retreat of the land up to 10 to 20 feet a year, and in exceptional storms cliffs have been pushed back by as much as 90 feet, where unconsolidated, loose sand and gravel were present. Parts of the east coast of England afford classic examples of such marine erosion. Maps of the area, some hundreds of years old, show towns where there is now only ocean, perhaps marked by a sandbar far offshore. Wave attack on resistant rocks may undercut a sea cliff and in some cases form caves penetrating deep inland, such as are to be found on the north Cornish coast of England.

The presence anywhere of a sea cliff is clear evidence that erosion has occurred and is occurring today. Current sea level was essentially established about 4,000 years ago. In addition to cliffs, the various ocean deposits, such as beaches and bars, which are now at sea level must also have been formed in this relatively brief period.

Rocks vary greatly from place to place in their resistance to erosion, and thus the wave-eroded shorelines of the world are never perfectly straight; the softer material is removed readily, leaving the more resistant behind for a later, delayed removal. In this way headlands and isolated rocky remnants surrounded by water may be carved. Sea stacks were formerly parts of the mainland and under water they are still attached to it. Along any coast where there are such stacks, the old ones are in the process of removal and new ones are constantly being formed. Such erosional remnants are found all around the world, wherever waves attack a shore of moderately hard rock which will stand up against the action of the sea for some time. The Pacific coast of the United States is especially rich in such features, and here too there are sea arches, formed when a stack has been cut through near water level.

The production of any wave-cut cliff implies the concomitant formation of a wave-cut platform lying at the base of effective surf erosion, which, if sea level should drop, will be left as an elevated terrace. The inner margin of such a raised terrace is marked by a cliff, and more rarely a former sea stack will rise above the eroded surface. Such elevated terraces are common along the Pacific coast of the United States. At the Palos Verdes Hills of southern California a series of levels one above another mark successive stands of the sea.

In its work of erosion and deposition the ocean produces very typical features along the shore. Sand, gravel, and mud are dumped to make beaches and bars varying greatly in form and size. Such deposits may be along shore, they may lie offshore, or they may be hooked onto the mainland at one end, forming sand spits. Offshore sand beaches and bars are typically found along the coast of New Jersey and further southward on the Atlantic and Gulf coasts. The end of Cape Cod and Sandy Hook off New Jersey are excellent examples of sand spits. Islands are sometimes connected to the mainland by a sandy beach or tombolo. Lynn and Nahant beaches north of Boston, Nantasket to the south, and the beach connecting Morro Rock to the California mainland are examples of such features. In the case of Nantasket a number of drumlins were partially destroyed by wave action and the resulting material was spread out to form a deposit which eventually joined them to the mainland. The sand along many beaches has been refashioned by the wind into dunes of various shapes and sizes which may locally form the major relief features. All shore deposits are constantly being modified with ever changing shapes and locations due to the continued action of waves, currents, and wind.

Material is moved along a beach whenever a series of waves hit the shore at an angle. As the waves break they will take particles of sand or gravel up the beach with a slight component along the shore in the direction of wave motion, and as the wave retreats the particles will be moved straight down the beach slope. Thus each time a wave comes in and retreats a particle will find itself displaced slightly from its initial position. Any breakwater is likely to show a buildup of loose material on the windward side and a removal on the leeward.

Whether a specific part of the coast is being removed or built out depends upon a variety of factors, such as the direction of the prevailing winds, the configuration of the shore, the way in which currents and tides are effective, and the supplies of debris being brought to the sea by the local rivers. The continued abundance of sand along any stretch of beach requires the necessary replenishment of material from elsewhere.

Loose material along the shore is characteristically well sorted, that is, the coarse materials are separated from the fine. Furthermore, the larger particles of sand and gravel are well rounded by mutual abrasion. At times of high waves, it is easy to hear the grinding of the pebbles, one against the other, as the surf breaks and retreats. At times of maximum turbulence when waves are high, the ocean carries much material in suspension. The coarser particles are rolled and pushed along the bottom in a stormy sea. Man has made desperate attempts at various places to control the destructive action of the sea and to keep open channels which are constantly being filled in by sand and mud. Geologic processes, however, are supreme, and all that can be done for a few generations at most is to control the motion of materials along a short stretch of the coast.

The ocean is the resting place of material washed off the land, and the marine origin of most of the world's sedimentary rocks is indicated by the presence of sea organisms found as fossils. The sedimentary rocks now found in the land must represent but a very small part of the mud, sand, and gravel beds that were continually being laid down and then lost in the shifting shores of the advancing and retreating seas of the past.

Over 50 per cent of the volume of all sedimentary rocks is shale. Sandstone forms about 20 per cent and limestone most of the remainder. The type of deposits, however, currently being laid down offshore is just the opposite; most is sand and the least is mud. This poses a problem. It may only be a short-term phenomenon. The widespread rise in sea level in the recent past, since the continental glaciers melted, may have resulted in a greater than average erosion of new land areas and the deposition of sand to a larger extent than usual in the past.

An analysis of the types of material mantling the shallow sea floor off southern California indicates various origins. There are patches of beach and dune deposits, relics of an earlier environment now submerged, and bits of organic debris, shells of various types. Certain areas show deposits which were laid down directly by precipitation from seawater, such as a variety of phosphorous-bearing minerals. Residual deposits, or those weathered underwater from underlying rocks, occur locally; and widely scattered, filling in the lower parts of the sea floor, is detrital material supplied from the land and washed out into the sea by wave and current action. These deposits taken alone seem to grow finer as one goes seaward, the coarsest materials such as gravel being closest to the land, and then sand and mud farther out. The land source of this material is from rivers, deltas and eroded sea cliffs, and beaches.

Underwater deposits of sand, shaped like wind-produced sand dunes and with a somewhat similar origin, are to be found in a number of places. Most of them lie perpendicular to the direction of water currents, although some of the longest are ridges which stream parallel to it. They vary in wave length, or distance from crest to crest, from a thousand feet or so, up to a mile or more. The side from which the current comes slopes very gently, about 2 degrees, and the lee slope is 18 to 20 degrees. Such an asymmetric profile is also characteristic of wind-formed dunes. Wherever a moving current, either air or water, brings material up a gentle dune slope to the crest it will drop it over this crest on the lee side, where it forms a much steeper slope at the angle of repose of the materials being carried. Some sand waves are symmetrical and represent an ebb-and-flow phenomenon where the current comes first from one direction and then from another.

Sand waves occur where there are topographic protuberances or constrictions which cause strong bottom currents. For instance, they have developed at the entrance to Delaware Bay and in some of the major rivers such as the Mississippi and the Columbia. The waves in the Mississippi River at Helena, Arkansas, have a height of 22 feet and a length of 1,000 feet between crests. The sand waves themselves migrate, being shifted downstream by the slow removal of material from the upstream side over the crest to be dumped on the downstream side. At times of very turbulent high water the motion of the crest may be up to 80 feet per day.

The sand waves found on George's Bank, an immense bar at the entrance to the Gulf of Maine, are up to 50 feet high. They are found on top of the various shoals, where the water is only 100 feet or so deep, and where the current may run up to 20 knots at times of strong hurricane winds.

The most impressive characteristic of today's coastlines is their great irregularity. The contact between land and sea may be very tortuous, and distances along the shore are in most cases many times the airline distances from one coastal location to another. The coast of Maine, for instance, is roughly 230 miles long, but the detailed tidal shoreline as measured on large-scale maps is 3,480 miles. Even on such a coast as that of California, which seems to be relatively straight, the analogous distances are 840 and 3,430 miles.

On a visit to the coast of Maine one can see that at the present time the deep bays are being filled in at their landward ends by river deposits, while many of the outer promontories of this indented coast have been notched with sea-formed cliffs. The many islands so notable in the Casco Bay area are much larger than the average sea stack of the California coast and are in general much farther offshore. They could never have been formed by the erosion of the material between them and the mainland. Only the outermost margins are now being attacked by the sea, and the area behind is in many cases being filled in with deposits. These islands appeared when a land of hills and valleys was inundated by a rise in sea level. The hills now stand as islands and the valleys, flooded in their seaward extremities, now appear as the estuaries which deeply penetrate the land. The ridges on the land which extend seaward into the promontories, which in turn extend still farther as a string of islands and as underwater rock ledges, are composed of more resistant material than that which underlies the valleys. In many places in the estuaries the lobster fishermen have brought up bits of peat and decomposed grass roots with their traps from these flooded stream valleys. Further south along the Atlantic Coastal Plain, Chesapeake Bay with its tributary inlets reflects the dendritic stream pattern which existed there before the ocean drowned the seaward end of the Susquehanna River system.

Irregular shorelines, wherever they are found, are explained by the drowning of an irregular land area carved by various agents of erosion, particularly streams. The arrangement of the estuaries, inlets, and islands shows the predrowning nature of the topography of the land, which in turn, of course, reflected the structure.

Marine erosion does produce irregularities of the coastline, as we have seen, in the shape of headlands and sea stacks where the rocks are a trifle more resistant and coves where the rocks are softer. These irregularities, however, are measurable as a few thousand feet at most compared with the many miles associated with the drowning of a hilly landscape such as that of Maine.

Whenever the sea comes in contact with the land it will start to produce its own characteristic features, the wave-cut cliff and sea stack, and will deposit material in various forms as bars, tombolos, or spits. Obviously, the longer the ocean has worked on the land at any one level the more prominent will be the ocean-produced features, and wherever the sea has relatively soft material to work with, it will dominate the coastal landscape much more quickly than where hard rock exists. This is well shown in comparing the landscape of the Maine coast with that of Massachusetts. In Maine the ocean has hard granites and metamorphic rocks to deal with and its impact on the coastal scenery has been relatively slight since the last rise in sea level. Farther south along the Massachusetts shore the land was flooded at approximately the same time, but here there are softer materials—drumlins, glacial outwash, and moraines—and the sea has destroyed and obscured the drowned aspect of the land much more noticeably than farther north.

In summary, the explanation for the shape of any coastline rests on two considerations, the topography before change of sea level and the work of the sea on it. First, the major shape of a coastline is explainable in terms of the configuration of the predrowned landscape, whether it be river system, fiord, glacial deposits, or any other landscape features caused by any erosional agents, or volcanic activity, or, very rarely, diastrophism. Second, ocean-produced features, both erosional and depositional, tend to obscure and modify the shape of the coastline, initially explainable in terms of predrowning happenings.

Evidence for a changing relationship between land and sea is extensive. Most large rivers leading into the sea are characterized by broad floodplains where drilling shows a thick alluvial fill. Such depth of fill extending far below any present-day cutting of the streams is easily explained by deposition following a rise in sea level and the flooding of the lower reaches.

On the coast of Italy a little north of Naples, at Pozzuoli, the marble columns of the Greek temple of Serapis have small holes in them 15 to 20 feet above the present level of the Mediterranean. These holes were drilled by boring clams at a time when the columns were obviously covered by water. They are clearcut evidence of the drowning and later partial re-elevation of this region of the world since classical times.

Off New York City the outer part of the continental shelf is marked by a 480-foot-deep wave-cut bench, formed probably at the time of the Illinoisian glacial advance, when sea level was much lower than it is now. This bench has been filled with more recent sediments, but its location and the evidence for its presence have been obtained by geophysical techniques. In Long Island Sound the bedrock is 600 to 700 feet below sea level, and has been covered by a thick layer of recent sediments so that the depth to the sea bottom is much less than to bedrock. Long Island Sound was undoubtedly cut by subaerial streams and was then drowned by a rise in sea level.

Further evidence for recent flooding of many areas of the world has been obtained with the help of radiocarbon dating. Along the Connecticut shore in the Clinton area there has been a 9-foot submergence in the last 3,000 years and a 33-foot submergence of the land in the last 7,000 years. The evidence is based on the burial, below sea level, of plants of the type which grow on the landward margin of salt-water marshes.

There is no doubt about a rise of sea level following the melting of the last glacial advance. There are various opinions, however, with respect to the relative rapidity of this rise and when it actually occurred. The use of different data and various interpretations can easily lead to conflicting ideas. Some geologists have suggested that about 4000 B.C. there was a very rapid rise of approximately 45 feet within a few centuries. Such a rise might explain the biblical and Buddhist records of floods.

Many coasts of the world present evidence of having been both higher and lower with respect to sea level than they are now. The Pacific coast of the United States, in addition to elevated wave-cut terraces, cliffs, and beach deposits, also has features due to drowning, such as San Francisco Bay and Puget Sound.

If sea level dropped a mere 150 feet Alaska and Sibera would be connected via the Bering Straits area. Inasmuch as more than a 150-feet drop was undoubtedly associated with the times of maximum glaciation, there must have been a land bridge here each time the ice built up on the land. Actually paleontological evidence shows a land bridge throughout most of the Cenozoic Era. A land connection formerly cut off the Arctic Ocean from the northern Pacific, with the result that the types of marine life in each area became dissimilar, while the land life of the two continents became alike.

Evidence for profound shifting of the land with respect to the sea in the more distant past lies in such observations as finding sedimentary rocks containing marine fossils thousands of feet up in some of the major mountain ranges of the world, such as the Himalayas, the Appalachians, and the Rockies. It is probable that the oceans at one time or another have covered every part of the earth which is now dry land.

Away from the coastline beneath the oceans there is a great

variety in topography, the details of which are beginning to be discovered by means of supersonic echo sounders. A shallow shelf zone surrounds most continents. Here the water on the whole becomes gradually deeper away from the land to a varying depth, generally 200 to 600 feet, where the relatively steep Continental Slope commences. The gradient of the Continental Slope averages about 5 degrees in contrast to the average Shelf slope of less than 1 degree. The Slope descends to a depth between 3 and 10 thousand feet, and at its base is a lessened declivity called the Continental Rise, beyond which lie the ocean basins.

The Atlantic Continental Shelf extending from the Maritime Provinces to the Gulf of Mexico has aspects characteristic of many shelves of the world. The depth of water at the transition from shelf to slope varies. Off Florida it is somewhat less than 200 feet, off the New England coast it is 400 to 500 feet. The Shelf is, on the whole, narrower off Florida and wider off New England. Very roughly speaking the Continental Shelf plus the Coastal Plain are more or less constant in combined width. The surface of the Shelf is moderately irregular, especially so in the northern parts where there are glacial deposits such as drowned moraines and drumlins. Much of the Shelf was subject at one time or another to stream erosion when sea level was lower, and thus irregularities due to valley incision are also inevitable. Submerged wave-cut cliffs are found, as well as sand waves, as we have seen.

The Continental Rise at the base of the Slope is a broad apron which is probably in large part a fan of debris, deposited by currents flowing down the Continental Slope and resembling in this respect a series of alluvial fans at the base of a mountain range. The widespread floor of the Ocean Basins starts at the foot of the Continental Rise and in general consists of regions of abyssal hills collectively giving areas of low hilly topography, and very flat areas, the abyssal plains. The plains apparently are areas where sediments have smothered an underlying hilly topography, and they generally lie adjacent to the Continental Rise. Off the Atlantic coast of North America the abyssal plains lie at a depth of about 17,000 feet.

Submarine canyons, which are incised into continental slopes are found off all continents and their origin is still somewhat of an enigma. They have rock walls cut into bedrock of all degrees of hardness from granite to much softer types, and they have winding courses with dendritic tributaries. They are not necessarily associated with large rivers flowing into the sea, but they may be. The Hudson River Canyon is in line with the Hudson River exit on the Continental Shelf and its short submerged channel there. The walls

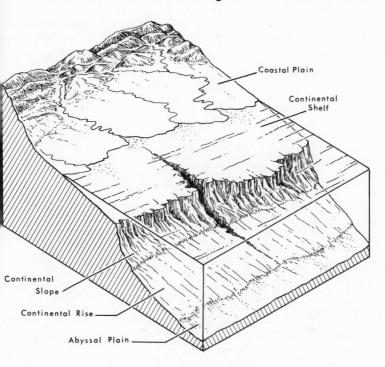

A typical continental border

of submarine canyons are generally V-shaped in profile, and there is often a layer of sand and gravel at the bottom. Apparently the rock-walled sections of the canyons end part way down the Continental Slope, although many valleys continue across the fans at the base of the Slope as channels confined between natural levees. Most submarine canyons head into the Continental Shelf and some may start essentially at the coast; they extend more than a mile under present sea level.

A relatively recent lowering of sea level of over a mile would expose the shelf and slope, and the canyons could be cut by streams. There is no mechanism, however, which is generally acceptable that will lower sea level this much during such a short length of geologic time. Thus the necessity for having the canyon cutting done below sea level is obvious, and of the various meth-

(Modified in part from Heezen)

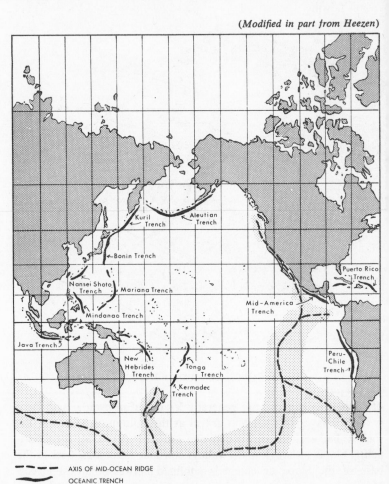

- – – – AXIS OF MID-OCEAN RIDGE
- ——— OCEANIC TRENCH

Mid-ocean ridges and deep-sea trenches

ods which have been suggested that of currents of dense, turbid water flowing down the slopes in an environment of less dense, clear water seems to be the most acceptable at the present time. That turbidity currents do actually occur has been demonstrated in a number of places. As early as 1885 such currents of turbid water flowing through otherwise clear water was noted in the Lake

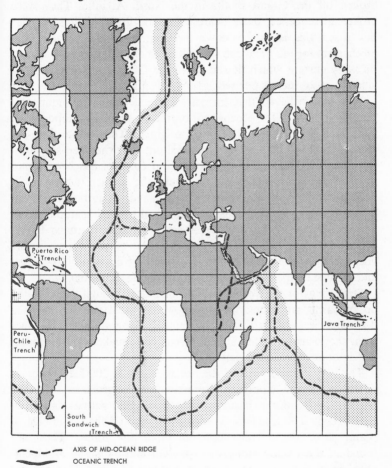

---- AXIS OF MID-OCEAN RIDGE

⌣‿ OCEANIC TRENCH

of Geneva. In Lake Mead in Arizona the mud-laden waters of the Colorado River at times of flood enter the head of the lake and have appeared near the dam, miles away. Turbid water with densities as low as $1.006gr/cm^3$ have been found to flow quite readily down relatively gentle slopes with velocities starting at 25 centimeters per second. In 1929 a number of submarine cables were broken off the Grand Banks in the North Atlantic. They were broken in sequence, those nearest the land first and those farther out to sea, that is, farther down the Continental Slope, later. The mechanism for the breakage was later demonstrated to have been a turbidity current which flowed down the Continental Slope with a velocity of 20 meters per second.

It is now believed that turbidity currents dominate sedimentation in all parts of the oceans, not barred by submarine topography from such slopes where they might originate. They create deep-sea alluvial fans and have spread material out over the deep-sea abyssal plains. Sedimentation by such turbid currents has been found on the bottom thousands of feet below the surface, where crossbedding and ripple marks have been noted. A turbidity current probably starts when a mass of rapidly deposited material in an unstable condition on a slope is set in motion, perhaps by an earthquake. The rate of deposition by these currents is obviously very much faster than that of sedimentation from wind-blown dust and organic debris raining down on the deep-sea bottom.

Stretching for tens of thousands of miles through most of the ocean basins are submarine ridges, which rise from the deep-sea floor and are usually topped by faulted topography. Such ridges form the locus for many shallow-focus earthquakes and a moderate amount of volcanic activity.

The very deepest parts of the oceans, over 20,000 feet, occur as relatively narrow, elongated depressions in the sea floor, near the borders of the ocean basins where diastrophic activity has been most recent. The trenches lie adjacent to and on the ocean side of island arcs, or actively uplifted mountain zones. They are found in the Pacific along the Aleutian and Japanese archipelagoes, near Sumatra and Java in Indonesia, along Mexico and Central America, and along stretches of the South American coast. None occurs off Canada and the United States. In the Atlantic they are less extensive, the Puerto Rico Trough being perhaps the most notable.

Such downwarped parts of the crust, with their associated island arcs or mountain chains, are some of the most diastrophically active geologic structures on the earth's surface today. They mark the greatest depths of the ocean and are associated with pronounced volcanic and seismic activity.

Individual trenches are remarkably continuous and uniform for long distances, up to 1,000 miles or more. They are narrow, perhaps 50 to 60 miles wide at most. The transverse profile of the average trench is asymmetric, with the steepest slope toward the land. The Tonga Trench, for instance, in the western Pacific slopes upward on its west side 8 to 15 degrees, toward various island groups and eventually Australia. Toward the east and the open ocean the slope varies from 3 to 8 degrees.

Scattered widely in the abyssal parts of the seas, away from the shelves, ridges, and trenches, are isolated mountain elevations, so-called sea mounts. They rise above the average elevation of the sea floor and form the major relief features in these otherwise more or less featureless areas. Sea mounts are probably in most cases volcanoes. Some have not been built up to sea level, and some are cones whose tops have been eroded to a flat platform, now submerged one to two kilometers below the ocean level. These are the so-called Guyots, discovered by H. H. Hess in the Pacific in 1946 and named after Arnold Guyot, Swiss geographer and associate of Louis Agassiz. They are interesting features in that they give striking evidence of diastrophic activity in that area. In a number of cases rounded cobblestones are found on the top, obviously shaped by wave and surf action when the cones were at sea level. Most characteristically there is a very abrupt change from a flat top to the flanks which slope downward 15 to 40 degrees. The presence of Guyots demonstrates a change of one to two kilometers in the depth of the ocean, owing primarily to local dropping of the sea floor, aided by some rise in sea level connected with the postglacial change.

Atolls, closely allied with sea mounts in their probable origin, are typically ring-shaped reefs with shallow lagoons at the center. They vary in shape from circular to elliptical to rectangular. Over

330 have been found in the world, most of them in the southwest Pacific. Atolls consist of a framework of coral with much lime added from lime-secreting plants and invertebrate animals, all built on a volcanic platform, perhaps a guyot. The lagoon at the center of the atoll varies in depth to a number of fathoms, the average about 25. Many coral knobs are present—some very flat areas, and some areas of lime, sand, and mud. On the seaward side of atolls there is a submarine talus slope of broken coral and limy debris.

The cause of the development of atolls has long been a problem. One of the earliest theories concerning their origin was that suggested by Charles Darwin. He suggested that they started as volcanic islands with fringing coral reefs, that subsequently the islands sank, and that as they did so, the reefs were built upward to the surface if the subsidence was not too rapid. In time the volcano around which the original coral reef was formed would sink below ocean level and the upbuilding coral reef, now an atoll, would be all that was left. The results of drilling into a number of atolls seem to bear out this theory. In the Eniwetok Atoll three holes were drilled in 1951-1952; the two deepest were 4,222 and 4,630 feet deep, respectively, and went through 4,000 feet of shallow-water reef limestone before entering basalt, similar in composition to that found on many Pacific volcanic islands. At the bottom of the 4,000 feet of limestone the fossils were dated as Eocene in age. This represents an average rate of subsidence of $\frac{4}{5}$ of an inch every 1,000 years for the 60 million years elapsing since Eocene time.

At the Bikini Atoll five holes were drilled in 1947, through poorly consolidated to unconsolidated reef materials all the way. The deepest hole was 2,556 feet. Again the evidence demonstrated conclusively that the Pacific sea floor, in the vicinity of the atolls at least, is certainly unstable, with very marked subsidence in the Cenozoic Era.

Sediments found in oceans near the continents and islands are essentially of land origin. Elsewhere, where turbidity currents have not carried material downslope away from the land, there are wide areas of so-called oozes, both calcareous and silicious, and red clays. The oozes are of organic origin, either plant or animal, and accumulate at an extremely slow rate, probably on the average no more than 1 to 10 millimeters per 1,000 years. Thus individual particles in such a deposit may be exposed for hundreds of years at the sediment-water interface, and be subject to marked changes in that environment.

Cores from the deep-sea bottoms in both the Pacific and Atlantic oceans show in a majority of cases discontinuous sedimentation, undoubtedly caused by downslope slumping. Turbidity currents, or the stirring up of the bottom material by various organisms. In the higher latitudes there is much material of glacial origin on the bottom, either pushed out from the land by former glaciers or frozen in icebergs and rafted out to the open sea, to be dumped when the icebergs melted.

Most economically useful mineral deposits from under the sea come from the shelf area at the present time. The principal resources are oil and gas, which have been widely found and exploited. In places, as on the Gulf coast, sulphur has been extracted from the caprock of salt domes found offshore. Other shelf deposits, formed as beach placer deposits, are now buried under a rising sea, and may mark concentrations of such heavy durable materials as gold off Alaska, tin ore off Malaysia, diamonds off the southwest African coast, and magnetite sand off Japan.

Seawater itself is a very lean "ore," since only some of the common salts are readily available for extraction. Many cubic miles of seawater would have to be processed to obtain a reasonable amount of many of the commonly used metals. In all the seawater of the world, however, staggeringly large amounts of various materials exist in solution. For instance, it has been calculated that there are altogether 16 billion tons of copper, 7 trillion tons of boron, 15 million tons of manganese, 20 billion tons of uranium, and 10 million tons of gold scattered throughout all the oceans of the world.

One of the very interesting deposits found on the sea floor is the nodules of manganese oxide, which are of potential economic importance as a source for manganese as well as for small amounts of cobalt, iron, and nickel. The nodules are porous deposits, and generally range in diameter from one to nine or ten inches. They often form around a bit of clay and display an onionskin type of layering, owing to the slow deposition of material on the surface.

They are found well away from land and are relatively widely distributed on many parts of the sea floor.

The oceans at the present time are being actively explored for many different kinds of information. The tie-in of the less well-known geology of these areas with the continents is vital in the attempt to answer many of the fundamental problems of earth history and structure.

CHAPTER IX

GLACIERS

A glacier is a mass of ice on the land which gives evidence of flowage. It originates from the compaction as well as the partial melting and subsequent refreezing of snow, and its formation is inevitable if over a number of years more snow falls during the winter than melts in the summer. In general this situation exists today in the polar regions and the higher colder areas of the world where there is adequate precipitation. Well-developed glaciers are now found in Antarctica, Greenland, Alaska, the northern Rockies, the Alps, parts of Norway, the Himalayas, and on various other high mountains, some even in equatorial regions.

On traveling either northward or southward from the equator, or up into the mountains, the snows of the winter are seen to last longer and longer into the spring, until, if the elevation is great enough or the distance traveled poleward is adequate, a place will be reached where piled-up winter snow will not entirely melt the following summer. This marks the snowline, or the transition from an area where there is always some snow left throughout the year to where, generally speaking, the snow entirely disappears in the summer, or perhaps does not appear at all. It is thus only above the snowline that glaciers can form.

Almost 10 per cent of the land areas of the world lie above the snowline, the location of which is controlled by both the amount of snow precipitation and the average temperature. On the northern

(Bradford Washburn)

Barnard Glacier and Mount Bona, Alaska. Typical glacier-formed, jagged

tip of Greenland, for instance, in Peary Land, in an area as large as Maine there is no ice cover. Here the precipitation is so small that even though the year-round temperature is relatively low no glaciers will form. The same situation also prevails in the Central Alaskan Lowland between the Brooks Range on the north and the Alaskan Range on the south. Even at times when glaciers were most widespread over North America this area was not covered by ice. The precipitation of snow was too small for the formation of glaciers.

The highest snowline in the world is in the Andes, at 21,000 feet. In the Olympic Mountains of Washington it reaches the lowest elevation of any point in continental United States, lying at 6,000 feet above sea level. It is low here because of the heavy snow fall. On Mount Shasta in California the line is at 13,500 feet and farther south at Popocatapetl in Mexico it lies between 16,000 and 17,000 feet.

The front of any glacier must reach an elevation below snowline before it disappears entirely. The position of the ice front here depends on the rate of supply of new ice flowing down from above the snowline and the rate of wastage, that is, melting and evaporation. The quantity of new ice which accumulates above the snowline depends, of course, on the rate of precipitation of snow and the average temperature there. At times the front of a glacier may rather suddenly advance. Such a surge reflects a larger than usual addition of snow in the area of accumulation a few years before, which might, for instance, be due to extensive avalanching, set in motion possibly by an earthquake.

The quantity of water which lies on the land in the form of ice is enormous, probably over 4,500,000 cubic miles. Antarctica, with an area of over 6 million square miles and an average thickness of ice cover of more than a mile, is the home of approximately 90 per cent of all the ice in the world and, incidentally, 64 per cent of all the world's water outside the oceans. The Antarctica ice, if entirely melted, would be adequate to keep the Mississippi River flowing for 50,000 years. Again, if the ice melted, the oceans of the world would rise by perhaps as much as 200 feet. There is clear evidence that ice was not always present on Antarctica. Numerous coal seams from the late Paleozoic represent deposits laid down when vegetation covered this now barren land.

Glaciers appear as sheets and streams. Ice sheets include the continental masses which now cover Antarctica and Greenland and formerly covered large parts of North America and Scandinavia, as well as the smaller icecaps on the Arctic islands off Canada, and the high-level plateau glaciers of Norway. They are nourished directly by snow and they flow outward from the center of accumulation, the general level of ice sloping downward from a high central point. The topography of the land under such cover may be very irregular indeed and the ice at the bottom may be forced up and over hills by the pressure of the overlying ice.

Streams of ice include all valley- and Alpine-type glaciers nourished in their upper reaches by snow accumulation and also the outlet glaciers which spread outward and down from icecaps and continental masses through gaps and valleys in the surrounding terrain.

One other type of glacier which might be included, as a special case, in the ice-sheet category, is the Piedmont glacier, which is formed by the coalescence of a number of valley glaciers at their extremity, and which spreads out as a semistagnant mass at the foot of a mountain range. The Malaspina Glacier of Alaska is a classic example of this type.

Various landscape features associated with present-day glaciers are obvious in their origin. For instance, scratches found on the bedrock immediately in front of a retreating glacier must have been produced by boulders frozen in the bottom of the ice when it was advancing. Piles of debris, consisting of unsorted mud, sand, and gravel in varying proportions dumped directly in front of a glacier, were clearly carried by the ice and dropped when it melted. And large boulders found near the ice front were obviously glacier borne. Features such as these, when closely associated with a glacier, have an obvious origin, but geologists have only recently accepted the suggestion that similar features located many miles from existing glaciers, or in areas where there are no present glaciers, might have a similar origin. The presence of boulders and piles of debris was explained formerly by the coming of a catastrophic flood.

The history of the development of the glacial explanation for many landscape features starts with Ignace Venetz, a Swiss engineer. In 1821 he read a paper at the eighth annual meeting of the Swiss Society of Natural Scientists, in which he made the observation that moraines, that is, piles of mud, sand, and gravel all heterogeneously mixed together, were found far beyond the present-day Swiss glaciers; he suggested that they were deposited by former extensions of the current glaciers. A little later, in 1829, he pointed out the wide distribution of erratic boulders, not only in Switzerland but in northern Europe, and proposed their transportation by glaciers. Following him, Jean de Charpentier, a friend of Venetz, gave a talk in 1834 on moraines, erratics, and striae to be found near Lucerne in Switzerland. Louis Agassiz, a young Swiss scientist who became one of the best-known geologists of his time, was won over by Charpentier in 1836 to the glacial explanation for these features, and in 1840 he published his classic *Etudes sur les Glaciers de la Suisse*. Agassiz traveled widely in Europe and the United States. He found landscape features in England and the United States which he explained as having been fashioned by former ice sheets which have now entirely disappeared. Many deposits of sorted sand and gravel which could not possibly have been laid down by present-day lakes or rivers, lying as they did at altogether too high an elevation, were explained as melt-water deposits from the now vanished ice.

After the time of Agassiz glacial deposits have been investigated in many areas throughout the world, and there is clear evidence that ice covered extensive tracts of land four times in the last million years or so. At the times of maximum glaciation at least three times as much land was ice-covered as now.

Ice is a hard, brittle substance and breaks like glass, yet it flows down valleys and spreads outward from accumulating centers as if it were a very thick liquid. A glacier moves in this fashion because of a number of contributing factors. The brittle type of behavior is limited to the upper layer, generally not over 100 feet, which fractures and is crevassed, and which rides on the underlying layers and conforms to the turns in a valley by shifting and adjustments between separate blocks of ice. That the under parts of glaciers slide over their beds is demonstrated by the presence of grooving, striations, and polish on the bedrock. Evidence from boreholes shows that the extent of such slippage is highly variable, but probably accounts on the average for about 50 per cent of the total surface motion of the valley glaciers. In the bottom layers of the ice stream, melting followed by refreezing also contributes to motion. Since the melting point of ice is less under pressure, the lower parts of a glacier will melt on the up-valley face of protuberances in the bedrock and the water will then flow to refreeze on the down-valley face. The velocity of motion given by this process is limited by the speed with which heat liberated by refreezing can be conducted to the upstream face. The occurrence of recrystallization in glaciers is shown by the observation that the size of crystals increases with the amount of deformation and is markedly greater at the termini than near the source areas. Single ice crystals deform easily by slippage along atomic layers, and this factor also helps the motion of the ice to a variable extent.

The speed of glacial motion varies from a fraction of an inch per day to very exceptional rates of over 100 feet per day. Speed increases with temperature, the angle of the slope, and the depth of the ice.

A glacier does its job of erosion by using the load of debris which it carries as an abrasive tool to grind and pulverize the bedrock over which it slips, and also by freezing onto and plucking out loose chunks of rock, perhaps prepared for this operation by frost-wedging. Much material is ground into a fine powder and then carried away by meltwater. This very fine material in suspension, so-called rock flour, is responsible for the characteristic milky-green color of glacier-fed streams and lakes.

Glacial erosion is perhaps most obvious in mountain areas where two features are very noticeable, the cirque, or large amphitheater-shaped hollow fairly well up on the side of a mountain slope, and the wide U-shaped valley, formed by the passage of ice through a previously stream-cut valley.

The fashioning of any cirque starts when the climate changes and the snowline descends so that the upper end of a valley lies above it. A pile of ice develops and eventually becomes so large that it starts to move downhill under its own weight, following as it does so the line of least resistance, the narrow preglacial valley. As the upper end of the ice mass pulls away from the mountainside it

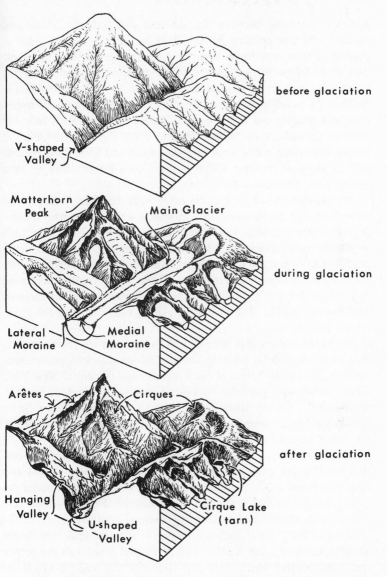

before glaciation

V-shaped Valley

Matterhorn Peak

Main Glacier

during glaciation

Lateral Moraine

Medial Moraine

Arêtes

Cirques

after glaciation

Hanging Valley

U-shaped Valley

Cirque Lake (tarn)

(From *This Sculptured Earth* by John A. Shimer. Permission of Columbia University Press)

Erosion of a mountain mass by valley glaciers

leaves an opening between the ice and the bedrock. Meltwater streams into this opening by day, and by night it freezes. Such a process of thaw and freeze inevitably breaks up the ledges of rock into small fragments, which are frozen in more ice as it forms in the crack, then to be carried away by the ice stream. In such a fashion, by freezing onto and removing shattered rock at the upper end, and gouging out at the base, a glacier literally eats a hole for itself in the side of the mountain, and when the ice disappears, a cirque with steep rocky head and side walls and a rounded bottom will be exposed to view. Often a small rock-floored lake or tarn appears on the floor of the cirque.

Ice flowing down a mountainside will tend to enlarge and straighten any previous stream-cut valley which it may be following. Glaciers produce U-shaped valleys because they ride high along the valley sides, scraping and gouging here as well as along the bottom. When the ice melts, any stream of water flowing in the former glacier-filled valley will not fill the valley to anywhere near the extent that the ice did, and the major part of the ice channel will thus be visible. The U-shaped glacial valley is truly the channel of the ice.

U-shaped valleys may also be produced when ice sheets in their marginal zones send probing tongues of ice out into pre-existing valleys. This is the origin of the Finger Lakes of central New York State, which now partially fill valleys that were oriented, roughly, north-south. Eleven lakes now drain to the north. They lie in elongated basins deepened by glacial scour and dammed up by morainal material at the southern ends.

The two largest lakes, Cayuga and Seneca, have bottom elevations below sea level. Seneca Lake has a water level at 444 feet and its bottom is 174 feet below sea level, while bedrock under the sediments is 600 feet lower still. It is believed that the western five lakes lie in valleys which probably drained southward before the coming of the glacier. Such a direction is strongly indicated by the configuration of Lake Keuka. This Y-shaped lake, with the principal stem pointed south, now fills two tributary valleys which undoubtedly were joined in such a manner that the acute angle pointed upstream or northward. In addition to the present Finger Lakes a number of north-south glaciated valleys are found in this area. They possess a flat floor of alluvium which changes to the sloping valley sides with a very abrupt junction, a modification of the original U-shape, brought about by later, postglacial river deposits partially filling the glacial valley.

U-shaped valleys are well illustrated by some of the through-going valleys in New Hampshire. For example, Pinkham, Crawford, and Franconia notches were all fashioned from preglacial valleys by the action of moving ice. Like all glacially modified valleys they are relatively straight and markedly different from typically tortuous stream-cut valleys.

Yosemite Valley, on the west slope of the Sierra Nevada Mountains in California, is one of the best known ice-fashioned valleys in the United States. The glacier has entirely disappeared and has left behind a wide valley with precipitous walls 3,000 to 4,000 feet high. Yosemite Valley possesses a wide, flat floor over which the Merced River meanders gently. This flat floor was produced in postglacial times when debris partially filled in the original U-shaped valley. Bedrock at Awahne Hotel, for instance, is approximately 1,800 feet under the alluvial fill, and near El Capitan bedrock is about 1,200 feet down. After the ice disappeared and uncovered this much deeper valley, a slightly sinuous finger lake was left because the ice had dug out the bedrock and a low morainal dam crossed the valley. Subsequently the erosion process was reversed and the lake was filled in by deltas built into it by the Tenaya and Merced rivers, producing the flat floor of the present Yosemite Valley.

The very rapid downcutting of the principal valley here was not matched by an equally rapid erosion of various tributary valleys. As a result, waters from the tributaries must drop into the major valley. The beautiful Bridal Veil Falls and Yosemite Falls exist because their valleys were left hanging in this way.

The contrast between the glaciated and unglaciated areas at Yosemite is striking. As one approaches from the west, as far as El Portal the road follows a narrow valley, where the traveler is forever aware of the steep sloping rock walls descending down to the road. The valley here has, roughly, a V-shaped cross-profile, the worldwide characteristic of geologic youth. A few miles above El Portal a dramatic change occurs: the valley opens out; the floor becomes much wider and the steep cliffs are much farther away from the road; it is here that the legacy left by the glacier is evident. The fact that the valley was cut into massive granite with very widely spaced joints has led to the development of steep, clean cliff faces. For example, the straight cliff under Glacier Point and the cliffs under the hanging valleys are all joint-determined.

Fiords, so beautifully developed along the Alaskan and Norwegian coasts, are essentially glaciated valleys which have been drowned at their seaward extremities by a rise in sea level. The Sognefiord on the Norwegian coast, one of the largest in the world, extends 120 miles back into the country. In places the floor of the fiord is 4,000 feet below sea level, the result of very deep glacial scouring.

A series of valley glaciers by a process of headward and lateral erosion may eat away at a mountain mass until only a serrate, jagged type of topography is left. Cirques forming on all sides of a peak may eventually leave nothing but a rock spire similar to the Matterhorn in the Alps, and fretted divides or aretes are left between cirques and glacial valleys if they are widened sufficiently. Such a type of topography, a landscape of cirques, Matterhorn peaks, and aretes, is now found in many places such as the Alps, the Alaska Range, the higher parts of the Grand Tetons of Wyoming, and the Sierra Nevada Mountains.

Mountain masses which are not so fully eroded glacially will show rounded upland surfaces into which cirque bites have been taken. The Mount Washington area of New Hampshire, the Uinta Mountains of Utah, and the Bighorn Mountains have this topography. The cirques so well developed on the flanks of the Presidential Range in New Hampshire must have been formed at a time when the mountaintops were above the snowline, both before and after the whole area was engulfed by the flood of ice from the north.

Erosional features due to glaciers on a smaller scale consist of glacial grooves, scratches, and polish given to rocks as the ice moves over them with its load of debris acting as an abrasive. Various asymmetrically shaped ledges also owe their smooth stoss face to the ice as it moved up and over the ledge, and the jagged lee side to the plucking action of the ice which froze onto bits of

broken or frost-shattered rock and carried them away. These gla-
cated ledges, known as roches moutonnées, may vary in size from
a few feet across to some hundreds.

It is to glacial erosion, then, that we turn for an explanation of
the worldwide Alpine type of scenery. Tongues of ice flow down
valleys previously fashioned by streams, gouge out and sharpen the
topographic profiles as they do so, and leave behind steep slopes,
rocky ledges, and sharp divides. Ice sheets, on the other hand,
generally do not sharpen the topography of the land but smooth it
off, inasmuch as they override hills and valleys alike, except of
course in hilly country like that of central New York State and
New England, where tongues of ice probing out in front of major
advancing ice sheets fashioned U-shaped valleys.

Outside the regions actually covered by ice, there is approximately 20 per cent of the land area of the earth (50 per cent of the
territory of Canada and the U.S.S.R.), where the mean annual
temperature is below freezing, and permanently frozen ground is
present. In such permafrost zones the ground stays frozen at depth,
and unfreezing occurs periodically from the surface down. This
condition is the reverse of the ordinary one in temperate regions,
where the ground is generally unfrozen but may freeze in the winter from the surface down.

The type of mass-wasting is markedly different in permafrost
regions and produces a unique series of soil structures, the result
of frost action in a saturated soil which cannot drain downward
because the material at depth is frozen. A typical type of soil
motion in such an environment is solifluction in which a mass of
water-saturated material on a slope flows down over ground frozen
at depth. Furthermore, soils under freeze-and-thaw conditions are
subject to much stirring up, which may result in the sorting of the
materials both vertically and laterally. Such action can be illustrated by analyzing the specific case of the rise of a boulder toward
the surface in a boulder-rich soil. On freezing, the whole mass of
soil with the contained boulder will expand, and on thawing contraction occurs. This results in the opening of a small hollow under
the boulder, which may then be partially filled with an oozing mass
of mud, or perhaps some sand or small pebbles may drop into the
cavity. Thus, on each freeze-and-thaw sequence the boulder is left

at a somewhat higher elevation than before. A similar freeze-and-thaw sequence enables variously shaped ice bodies to grow by pushing aside soil layers to make room for themselves. They may occur as horizontal layers, vertical wedges, or irregular masses in permafrost areas. Relicts of such ice bodies have been found outside present permafrost regions. For example, vertical ice wedges, filled in with slumped debris, have been found in northern Nova Scotia.

In places, in permafrost zones, the land may be decorated with piles of boulders arranged roughly in polygons, giving so-called patterned ground. The sorting of boulders from finer material is considered to be the result of many alternating freeze-and-thaw cycles. Fine silt and clay absorb more moisture than the coarser materials and, on freezing, push the gravel outward, away from the clay patches. On thawing, the clay contracts and the boulders remain where they were pushed. Another freeze enables the expanding clay to push the boulders yet farther away. Such polygonal piles of debris are found from a few inches to more than 30 feet across. If the sorting action occurs on a slope, downhill creep may elongate the polygons into more or less parallel stripes.

The debris, which is carried by a glacier and which is dumped when the ice melts, is called "till." It is a mixture of all the various-sized and -shaped materials that the ice has been carrying. In one deposit boulders, sand, and fine mud may be intimately mixed. Some tills may be primarily composed of rather coarse boulders, and others may be almost all mud and fine sand, the composition of any till depending upon the kind of rocks over which the glacier has traveled. An area of shales and limestones would supply easily broken materials and thus would give a muddy till. A region of granite or of hard metamorphic rocks, on the other hand, would give bouldery till. Boulders carried and deposited by ice, unlike waterborne boulders, are apt to be much more angular in outline, and they may also show striations and scratches on some of the faces.

Till is left piled in a great variety of forms. The terminal moraine is a deposit left at the extremity of a glacier. For instance, the eastern part of the continental ice sheet, which originated in Canada, extended as far south as Long Island before the ice melted, and on its way picked up much material in New England, which was dumped into the terminal moraine that now forms the hilly tract of land on the northern side of Long Island. The ice front at such a time was in a state of dynamic equilibrium. As fast as more ice was pushed from the north, the front melted backward, so that its position stayed essentially stationary, and the pile of debris grew higher and higher as more and more was added from the melting ice. At this time all the land northward to Canada was smothered by ice, and an air view of the area would have shown a white waste streaming southward.

The land on the south side of Long Island was never covered by ice. The outwash plain, which slopes gently from the ridge section southward to the sea, is composed of layers of sand and gravel, deposited by the glacial meltwater. At the time when the ice front was present at Long Island, sea level was much lower and the ocean shoreline was many miles to the south of its present location. Water streaming southward carried debris to this former seashore, so that at the present time much of the original outwash plain deposits are under the sea.

At the western end of Long Island near New York City there is only one morainal ridge, but toward the east it is divided, marking slightly different advances of the ice. This dual nature of the moraine is obvious in the drowned shoreline, where Montauk Point marks one moraine and Orient Point the drowned extremity of the other.

A large part of Cape Cod is similar in topography to Long Island, with a northern morainal part and a southern outwash area. The Cape Cod moraine and outwash were formed when ice was not as far south as its maximum extent, but had stopped briefly in its general retreat northward.

In many places the ice dumped its load of till as ground moraine which thinly covers large tracts of land. The hummocky, irregular surface so typical of moraines in general is often pitted with small hollows, now containing ponds and lakes. Many of these hollows are kettle holes, formed when a block of ice buried in the till melted, causing the surface to collapse and give a hollow. Kettle holes are roughly circular in shape and vary in depth from a few feet to well over 100.

Erratic boulders, some perched on the tops of rock ledges, and others buried in the soil, are characteristic features in many glaciated areas. Some can be identified as coming from a distinctive bedrock source, over which the glacier rode and from which it derived part of its load. Erratics are found most prolifically in regions of coherent, hard bedrock such as granite and metamorphics. Boulders composed of such material will stay together and not be crumbled in their ice travels, whereas shale and sandstone boulders do not survive nearly as well.

Till has been streamlined in places by the advancing ice to form elongated oval hills, drumlins. Characteristically they are 60 to 100 feet high and one-half to a mile in length. They commonly appear in groups, very rarely as isolated single features. In the Boston area they occur as oval-shaped islands in the harbor, as well as hills on the mainland. Other notable drumlin fields are to be found in New York State, just south of Lake Ontario, and in the Lake Michigan region.

In addition to the unsorted heterogeneous material which glaciers deposit as moraines, drumlins, and erratics, meltwater carries the mud, sand, and gravel fragments for some distance to lay them down in variously shaped bodies in sorted layers. This explains the presence of layers of water-worn pebbles and sand, obviously unconnected with any present-day river or sea, in areas once covered by ice. These sorted deposits take a number of forms. One of the commonest is the outwash plain such as those noted on Long Island and Cape Cod. Elsewhere, ridges varying in height from 20 to more than 100 feet and, extending for miles, may be found meandering sinuously through low-lying swampy areas. They are composed of roughly sorted coarse sand and gravel, which were laid down by streams flowing in cracks in stagnating masses of ice, or even under the ice. In either case the sides of the streambed were formed of ice, and when it melted away the material deposited by the stream was left as a ridge, known as an esker, rising above the surrounding country. In the swampy low country east of the Penobscot River near Bangor, Maine, there is a remarkable group of eskers, extending for miles, in a roughly north-south direction. Obviously, eskers must be associated in their genesis with a mass of ice which has stopped moving, and is merely melting. Moving ice which is being pushed from behind by a continually renewed supply would, of course, destroy the delicate, easily erased esker form.

Small conical hills of sorted sand and gravel, kames, are also associated with stagnating ice. They are formed either by streams flowing off the surface of the ice and building piles of debris right against the ice walls, or perhaps by debris filling a hole in the glacier. Kames and eskers make excellent sources of sand and gravel and both are frequently used for this.

A typical New Hampshire valley shows various meltwater deposits in the valley bottoms and part way up the sides, whereas till is found mantling the higher slopes and hilltops, where it has not been disturbed by the meltwater from the stagnant ice as it flooded the lower-lying areas. In addition to kames and eskers various other forms are found. They include delta deposits in glacial lakes now drained, and kame terraces, which are sand and gravel deposits now located on the sides of valleys, which were laid down when ice filled the valley bottom and meltwater flowed between the ice and the bedrock of the valley side. Further evidence for the presence of meltwater at an elevation well above present river and lake levels can sometimes be found in the form of potholes drilled into solid rock by swirling water with pebble tools, at a time when the valleys were filled with ice, and water was flowing at impossibly high elevations considering present-day levels.

Extensive moraines that loop across the country, drumlins, large areas of outwash deposits, eskers, and kames are uniquely connected with continental glaciers. The deposits associated with valley glaciers are far less extensive and consist of erratics, lateral and terminal moraines, and small outwash areas confined to the valley.

The center of accumulation of the North American continental sheet was roughly in the Hudson Bay region, and the ice oozed outward in all directions from here. That moving westward met the eastward moving Piedmont glaciers from the Rockies at the foot of the mountain slopes.

In New England and the central United States the ice came from the north and thus the moraines loop convexly toward the south, each loop corresponding to a major lowland down which the front advanced. Similarly in northern Canada, the moraines loop toward the north, since the ice came from the south here. They stretch across Baffin Island and the mainland toward the west.

Once one's attention has been called to the characteristics of glaciated country, whether it be erosional or depositional, there can be no doubt any longer that glaciers formerly covered many areas which are now totally free of them. Since the Cambrian there have apparently been only two times when ice masked appreciable portions of the land areas of the world. One occurred in the Permian and the second in the immediate past in the Pleistocene Epoch, which started about one million years ago.

Four times in the Pleistocene there was ice over much more country than there is today. Glaciers extended much farther down the mountains and spread over areas now free of ice. At maximum extent the continental glacier which mantled eastern Canada and northern United States reached southward to a line running from Long Island westward through northern Pennsylvania to the Ohio River, and thence down the Mississippi River to the Missouri River, and then up to within about 100 miles of the Canadian border. From this point it extended westward to the Rocky Mountains. In Europe, the Scandinavian ice sheet covered Norway, Sweden, Finland, and Denmark.

The last great worldwide advance of the ice was at a maximum approximately 18,000 years ago, and the final rapid disappearance of the ice from North America and Europe began 11,000 to 12,000 years ago. Since then all the continental glaciers have gone from these regions, although the disappearance was not continuous once it started. There were minor fluctuations, advances and retreats, with the retreats greater than the advances. There was a warm spell about 4000 B.C. when the ice retreated very rapidly. This was followed by a slight expansion around 500 B.C.; a recession during the time of the Roman Empire, to a period of greatly reduced glaciers about A.D. 1100. An advance of the ice again was noted about 1600 to 1850, and since 1850 there has been a general melting back of most of the world's glaciers. According to one glacialogist there is evidence for a total of 14 advances separated by retreats in the Alpine area between 1595 and 1939. In the 1920s and 1930s the retreat was quite marked in North America.

The evidence for a colder and wetter climate during the time of maximum ice in North America rests obviously on the investigation of the history of mountain glaciation, which shows the glaciers reaching much lower elevations than they do now. It also rests on the rise and development of lakes in basins which are dry at

The maximum extent of Pleistocene glaciers in North America

present. Such a lake was Bonneville, the greatly extended Salt Lake of Utah in the Ice Age.

At the time of the last maximum glaciation it is probable that man was present in North America and there is evidence that up to 8,000 years ago there were still elephants, camels, horses, and a large species of bison in the United States, at which time they died out rather abruptly. Some authorities feel that they were probably helped in their extinction by early man.

Changes in sea level associated with the coming and going of the major times of the Pleistocene ice age were marked. The third glacial advance, the Illinoisan, was probably 50 per cent more important than the Wisconsin, the last, and the volume of water locked up on land in the form of ice would have been a great deal more at such a time. At the Illinoisan time the volume of ice is considered to have been such as to have lowered sea level 450 to 520 feet. The variation in these figures refers to the two extreme estimates of the Antarctic ice volume, which is not known in detail. The lowering of sea level associated with the last glacial advance was probably between 340 and 400 feet. At these times of maximum ice development on land, the shoreline must have been many miles farther out on the continental shelves of the world.

It has been estimated that the melting of the south polar icecap would raise sea level by approximately 200 feet, but the added weight of water would make the ocean basins sink so the net rise would be less, perhaps only 130 feet or so. Incidentally, it has been reported that after the construction of Boulder Dam and the filling of Lake Mead where approximately 12 billion tons of water lies on an area about 30 miles across, the crust has sunk in places up to five inches, and accompanying the sinking there were a number of small earthquakes which obviously represented adjustments of the crust under such an added load.

At the times of maximum glaciation the weight of the ice concentrated in certain specific areas pushed the surface of the earth down. This is demonstrated indirectly by the postglacial rise of the areas which were so covered. In places in Scandinavia the rebound of the crust after the glacier left has been as much as 1,500 feet, and it has been suggested that there may be another 600 or 700 feet to go. Evidence for such rebound is given by wave-cut terraces and cliffs eroded just after the ice left, which are now elevated high above sea level. The rebound was obviously not immediate but somewhat sluggish.

In North America the sinking of the crust due to the load of ice was experienced as far south as a line between Long Island, Cleveland, and Milwaukee; and a maximum rebound of as much as 900 feet has been shown by raised wave-produced features somewhat east of Hudson Bay.

The large glacial lake, Lake Agassiz, which covered parts of Minnesota and North Dakota and extended up into Canada to cover a total area far more than the combined Great Lakes today, fashioned a shoreline of beach deposits and wave-cut cliffs. This shoreline was tilted toward the south by about 100 feet in a distance of 150 miles north to south, thus showing also an adjustment of the crust after the lake was drained when the ice dam at the northern edge melted away.

The one basic requirement for the formation of a glacier that more snow must fall than melts, can be met by climatic changes which do either one or both of two things: snow precipitation is increased or the average yearly temperature decreases. There is no generally accepted explanation for the required climatic changes which produce a time of glaciation. Some suggestions call in part on the sun being a variable star, and others on changes in the earth's atmosphere to block out the sun's heat energy reaching the earth or to allow a greater loss to space. The earth's atmosphere acts like the glass roof of a greenhouse. It traps the longer wavelength heat rays which are re-radiated from the surface. Water vapor and CO_2 are especially important in this action; therefore any diminuation of these constituents would allow more heat to be lost to space. On the other hand, a time of extensive volcanic activity might effectively fill the air with much volcanic dust, thus cutting off solar energy before it reaches the earth. Other suggestions call on some mechanism for increasing precipitation without necessarily changing the yearly average temperature.

Whatever their ultimate cause, glaciers have produced a profound effect on large parts of the world and given the final scenic modifications which are so prominent in many places. The very striking correlation all over the world between lakes and swamps and the former presence of glaciers is now explainable in terms of both ice erosion and the heterogeneous dumping of debris which in many areas largely destroyed preglacial lines of drainage.

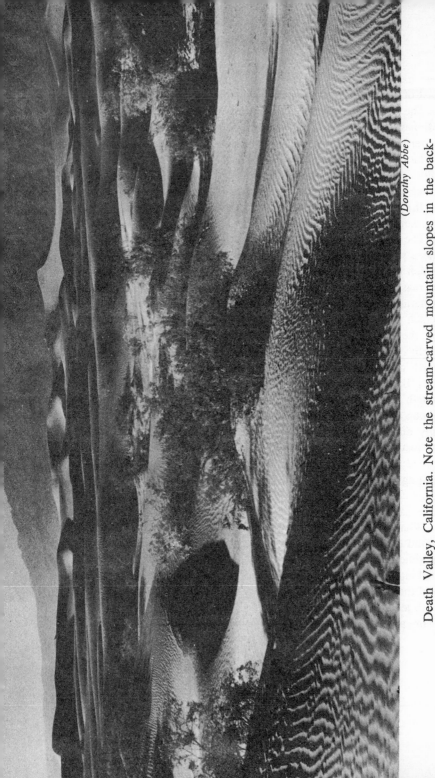

(Dorothy Abbe)

Death Valley, California. Note the stream-carved mountain slopes in the background and the wind-fashioned ripples and dunes in the foreground.

CHAPTER X

DESERT SCENERY AND THE
WORK OF THE WIND

The erosional work of the wind is most obvious in deserts where sand is not held down by a vegetation cover. Thus as a dominant agent of erosion wind is pre-eminent only in arid to semiarid regions where it moves dust, silt, fine sand and, under very strong wind conditions, moderately coarse sand.

The most obvious erosional landscape features caused by wind are the small hollows, blowouts, which are found in sand dunes, and the relatively large deflation hollows formed in loose materials such as the generally unconsolidated soil cover in the High Plains from Texas to Montana. These hollows are at times not very obvious because they are relatively shallow, at most a few hundred feet deep, and several square miles in area. A topographic map, however, will indicate them very clearly. Such selective removal of material can be started when a vegetation cover is removed by plowing or overgrazing.

The importance of the wind as an agent of abrasion, that is, of sand-blasting, is debatable, and many geologists feel that it is at most of minor significance. It undoubtedly has helped to produce some of the finer etched features found in desert areas, such as perhaps niches at the base of a desert wall. Of more importance, however, in the production of the intricately carved pedestal rocks, notches, and alcoves in cliffs in a desert is differential weathering, that is, weathering and breakup of certain parts of a rock mass more rapidly than other parts. The particles so formed are then removed by the rare rainwash, or by the wind. The sculpturing of rock ledges and cliffs anywhere is believed to be primarily the result of differential weathering rather than differential abrasion.

Wind transports material in much the same fashion as water does. The finer material is carried in suspension, and material of slightly larger size rolls and creeps along the surface of the ground, being similar to the bed load of a stream, and here and there one can spot sand grains which jump from one place to another. Such a jumping, or saltation process, depends on the motion of one grain, which on impact with another may impel it up into the air, where it will travel a short distance before landing. The motion of most wind-blown material is within a few inches, or very few feet at most, of ground level. In such travel sand grains are reduced in size and are rounded by mutual abrasion. Dust and very fine sand may be carried well up into the air and be blown hundreds to thousands of miles. Dust from Australia has been blown to New Zealand, a matter of 1,400 miles, and at times of storm, winds from the Sahara Desert have blown material over large parts of western Europe.

The most impressive and noticeable deposits of the wind are sand dunes, which are found along the coasts where sand is constantly being supplied by the ocean, along riverbanks, and in deserts where dried-up stream beds, alluvial fans, or weathered outcrops of sandstone supply material. Actually, sand covers only a small fraction of most deserts. The Sahara has an area of roughly $3\frac{1}{2}$ million square miles, of which less than $\frac{1}{7}$ is covered by sand dunes, the rest being stony or rock floored. Approximately 35 per cent of the Arabian Desert and 10 per cent of the deserts in the United States are covered by sand dunes.

Dunes appear in a fantastic variety of shapes and sizes. They vary from a few feet high, and a few feet across to many miles in length and 400 to 500 feet high, and in shape to include crescent, sigmoid, pyramidal, tuning fork, and hooked forms.

Where there is a prevailing wind, and a moderate supply of sand, crescent dunes, barchanes, may be formed. The points of the crescent stream with the prevailing wind direction. In some areas there are linear complexes of dunes, which parallel the wind direction, and elsewhere transverse dunes are found. The explanation for such variety in dune shape and orientation must lie in the interplay of many factors, among which the supply of sand, topography, and velocity and direction of the wind are important.

Moving dunes are characterized by a relatively gentle windward slope and a steep lee slope, the so-called slip face, which averages 20 to 30 degrees from the horizontal. This slope may in certain cases be up to 34 degrees, the maximum which dry sand can take without slumping. The windward slope may vary from 5 to 15 degrees. Moving dunes are also characterized by the production of high-angle cross-bedding. The wind carries material up the windward slope, over the top of the dune, at which point the sand settles down the slip face, to form steep layers on this leeward side. Then as the dune progresses forward these steeply tilted layers may be cut across and the material carried farther on to produce other layers. With slight changes of wind direction a dune may have a number of such steep layers intersecting at relatively high angles, and if a dune is buried under other deposits and solidified into a sandstone, the rock will of course show the bedding of the original dune. Such steep cross-bedding is a diagnostic characteristic of wind-blown sand deposits.

Dunes become fixed with a vegetation cover, and once the cover is removed they may start moving again. They may progress across country for many miles, overrunning forests and buildings, which will reappear if the supply of sand gives out as the dune field moves onward.

Another wind-formed deposit is loess, a fine permeable silt which consists primarily of microscopic angular particles of quartz, feldspar, and calcite. Extensive deposits are found in the central parts of the United States where, because the loess is composed of angular particles which interlock in a three-dimensional network, it will stand up as steep cliffs in roadcuts and along riverbanks. When it weathers it turns buff in color; unweathered it is gray.

Undoubtedly much of the loess in the world was orginally laid down in glacial outwash deposits which, on drying out, provided much fine material for the wind to move. Feldspar is not present in most sediments because in normal chemical weathering it is destroyed. The production of finely powdered feldspar, so common in loess, can be explained by mechanical glacial abrasion.

In desert areas where the supply of sand is limited, gravel plains or bedrock will be present. Plains of lag gravel are found on alluvial fans, and in various floodplain areas where the finer material has been carried away by the wind. The pebbles in such a gravel are smoothed by the abrasion of moving sand and given an enamel-like polish, desert varnish, by coatings of manganese and iron oxide. In rare instances some of the pebbles may show an obvious abraded surface, and instead of being rounded may have one or more flat sides. These pebbles are ventifacts, that is, wind-shaped stones.

In areas where potential evaporation exceeds precipitation, there is a scarcity of vegetation, obvious results of wind erosion and deposition, dunes where there is a supply of sand, and elsewhere, gravel or bedrock at the surface. Even here, however, gullies, water-worn slopes, and alluvial fans are very evident, the product of relatively rare rains.

In the United States, desert and semiarid areas are found in the Basin and Range Province of Utah, Nevada, and southern California, in parts of the Colorado Plateau Province, such as the Painted Desert, and in Oregon and Washington, east of the Cascade Mountains.

In temperate regions desert conditions prevail where the rainfall is less than 10 inches per year, and semiarid areas where the rainfall is between 10 and 20 inches per year. In Arctic areas precipitation can be very much less without the production of a desert. For instance, in northern Greenland, as we have seen, the precipitation is less than one inch per year. In equatorial regions, a greater amount of rainfall per year can occur, but a region will be desert, or at least semiarid, because of the greatly increased rate of evaporation.

The average river in a desert never reaches the sea. Streams are characteristically short, discontinuous, and intermittent. They start on the land and end on the land, as the water either flows into a transistory salt lake or dissipates into the dry ground. In rare cases, rivers such as the Nile and the Colorado, which rise outside of desert areas, have enough flow to survive the very large evaporation losses which occur as they traverse arid regions.

Contrary to widespread belief, the wind in deserts has moved a very small percentage of material compared with running water. Rainsplash, water cascading down a slope before it has reached a channel, and the many intermittent streams, though rarely flowing, do a tremendous job of erosion during the short periods of time when it does rain. Also, due to the sparseness of vegetation, water is not slowed up on the slopes as it would be in a more humid area. Deserts are regions of flash floods, where a generally dry streambed may very suddenly have a raging torrent in it following a heavy rainfall in the mountains. Such a flow quickly ebbs, and the stream will become dry again. Actually, in many deserts more water may fall in an individual rain than the statistical yearly average. This means that a year or more may pass without any rain at all.

In the Basin and Range country of Nevada a typical desert to semiarid type of landscape prevails. Here there are many north-south-trending mountain ranges with intervening valleys. The country is dry and desolate with far reaches to the mountain-ringed horizon. The valley basins have a very gentle slope downward from the steep encircling mountain fronts to a low spot in the center, in which there may be at times a salt lake. Many of the gentle slopes at the foot of the mountains are composed of rock-cut surfaces veneered with a very thin layer of debris, ranging from boulders to extremely fine clay in size. The gradient varies from 750 feet to less than 10 feet per mile. The origin of these so-called pediments is still somewhat controversial. They probably were cut by the lateral planation of streams or by sheet floods of water, coupled with the back-wearing of the mountain slope itself, by weathering and rainwash. In places alluvial fans appear at the base of the cliffs, such as those near Stove Pipe Wells in Death Valley. Here they form conspicuous piles of debris built of material carried down by the intermittent mountain streams.

On a detailed map of the Basin and Range country the traveler can note that some of the rivers vanish without reaching a body of water and that others flow down to the low parts of the basins to form lakes which may be ephemeral, disappearing in dry seasons. Such playa lakes leave salt incrustations when they dry out. Since all streams carry a small amount of material in solution and only fresh distilled water leaves such an enclosed basin, a concentration of soluble material is inevitable, and on drying out, an incrustation of salt will be exposed on the floor. Depending upon the type of material which is left the term borax lake, alkali flat, soda lake, salt lake, or even dry lake may be given to them.

The Great Salt Lake of Utah, the Dead Sea, and many other lakes scattered all over the world lie in basins with no outlet to the sea. The Great Salt Lake has varied markedly in size and volume in the last few generations. In 1870 it covered more than 5,000 square kilometers and had a depth of 15 meters. In 1963 the area was less than one-half this and the depth around nine meters. The slope of the lake bed and the shores is very slight, so that a moderate lowering of the level uncovers a correspondingly very large area. Slopes of less than two or three meters per kilometer occur on the average, many areas having a slope less than 20 centimeters per kilometer.

The water in Great Salt Lake is highly concentrated in a variety of salts, primarily sodium chloride. The inflow of water is mostly in the fall, winter, and spring, but recently has been less because much of the water in the inflowing streams has been used for irrigation. During the Ice Age there was a great deal more precipitation in this area than at the present time, and the Great Salt Lake and others were many times larger than they are now. At that time the Great Salt Lake spilled over to include the present Utah and Sevier Lakes, which are now isolated. This Ice Age lake, Lake Bonneville, left as evidence of its former presence derelict wavecut cliffs incised on the surrounding mountain slopes, as well as terraces, deltas, and sandbars. Now as we stand on the shore of the present greatly attenuated lake we can see such lines of terraces on the neighboring hills. They are especially conspicuous on the Oquirrh Mountains, just to the south of the lake.

CHAPTER XI

ROCK STRUCTURES
IN THE CRUST

The crust of earth, as we have seen, is in constant motion. Lava moves from one place to another, small weathered particles are carried by wind and water across the land, and rocks in the solid state are uplifted, twisted, and turned. This motion of the crust is rapid on the scale of geologic time, and is notably irregular in distribution, direction, and intensity. At the present time the earthquake belts of the world represent areas where diastrophism is most active.

The deformation of rocks may be accomplished elastically, plastically, or by rupture. All materials show some elasticity, the extent varying greatly from one to another. In elastic deformation an object returns to its original shape once the applied stresses have been removed. On the other hand, in either plastic deformation or rupture a material remains permanently changed in shape after the applied stresses have been removed. Tar and wax are examples of substances which can be plastically deformed. Given geologic time and the slow application of continuing forces, especially under high confining pressures, the shape of rocks and minerals can most easily be plastically altered. In such motion part of the deformation is accomplished by the recrystallization of the constituent materials, and part by both inter- and intra-granular shifting of

(E. Stebinger, U.S. Geological Survey)

Folded rocks in Glacier Park, Montana

material. If the rate of application of stress is fast enough, rocks will rupture, that is, break or shatter. Such a break is called a fault if relative motion of the material on either side has occurred, and a joint if no motion is evident. With variations in temperature, pressure, the rate of application of deforming forces and the type of chemical environment the boundary between the three types of deformation becomes quite variable for the same material. Although much has been found out about the behavior of rocks under various conditions in the laboratory, it is difficult to predict how a specific type of rock will react in a given geologic environment under long geologic time intervals.

There are two broad categories of earth movements, the epeirogenic and the orogenic. In epeirogenic movements (from the Greek *epeiros,* meaning a continent) there are broad movements of uplift and subsidence affecting a whole continent or at least an appreciable portion of one, or large part of the sea floor. That such movements have occurred is obvious, when changes in sea level in various parts of the world are considered. A study of the recent sediments in the Mississippi River delta area, for example, shows that there has been a subsidence here of more than 500 feet since the late Quaternary. On the Atlantic coast the Pre-Cretaceous erosion surface which separates the Coastal Plain sediments from the underlying material is now more than 10,000 feet below sea level on the Continental Shelf and would be some thousands of feet above sea level in the Appalachian Mountain area, where it has been entirely removed by more recent weathering and erosion.

Orogenies (from the Greek *oros,* meaning mountain) are localized, more intense disruptions in the crust, and are evident in folding and faulting. The location for such activity has changed widely throughout geologic history. Some of the most interesting and fundamental questions for geologists now are concerned with the attempt to explain a number of basic problems associated with orogenies, such as how are large mountain masses supported, why does land rebound so quickly after the removal of a major ice sheet, why does the position of diastrophic activity change throughout geologic time, what is the fundamental source of the energy needed and how is it applied to produce the results that we see? Some of these questions are still unanswered, while others have at least a partial explanation.

Folds are formed where forces act essentially parallel to the earth's surface. On the other hand, domes and basins can be produced by forces acting at right angles to the surface. Excellent examples of folded rocks are found in the Appalachian and Rocky Mountains, and domes and basins between these ranges in the Interior Lowland region where deformation has been less intense.

Rocks must be layered for folding to be evident, that is, they must be sediments, or the metamorphic equivalents of sedimentary rocks, or perhaps interbedded lava flows and sediments. Furthermore, the rate of deformation must be relatively slow and under the proper environmental conditions so that plastic deformation, not faulting, can take place. The massive rocks such as granite and large intrusive bodies will not show folding but can be jointed and faulted. Since sediments were initially in an essentially horizontal position, any deviations from this must represent the effects of diastrophism.

Upfolds, or anticlines, and downfolds, or synclines, may be either symmetrical or asymmetrical in cross-section and the folds may plunge; that is, the line along the top or bottom of the fold may not be horizontal. All imaginable combinations are found in regions of folded rocks. A thoroughly crumpled table cloth will give some idea of the possibilities. Generally anticlines alternate with synclines, the side or limb of an anticline having the limb of the neighboring syncline in common.

Joints are universally found in all types of rocks, and every outcropping ledge shows them. A joint generally occurs as one of a set of more or less parallel cracks and, as we have seen, it differs from a fault in that there is no relative motion of the rock masses on either side of the fracture. Joints may be only a few inches apart, or a number of feet. Most result from forces set up when the crustal materials are twisted, uplifted, and contorted. Columnar jointing in igneous flows, sills, and dikes, on the other hand, is the result of contraction on cooling. The curved exfoliation shells so well developed in Yosemite Valley are joints which are probably due to relief of pressure following the uncovering, by erosion, of the granite batholith here.

The presence of fractures, joints or faults aids greatly in both the mechanical and chemical breakup of solid rocks. They supply passageways down which water, carbon dioxide, and oxygen can penetrate deeply into a rock mass, and they form planes of weakness which control the configuration of cliffs, and on a larger scale may determine the location and pattern of river valleys. For instance, the rectangular shape of Lake Placid in the Adirondack Mountains shows the control which a system of fractures has exerted on the shape of the land. Here, there is a primary, and most important, northeast-southwest system of breaks which is crossed with a secondary system running at right angles. These systems have controlled the erosional development of the lake with its rectangular islands, as well as the location of the valleys and ridges in the surrounding area.

Faults, in the same fashion as joints, may form places where weathering is relatively easy, and thus determine the position and orientation of valleys and the alignment of cliffs. Furthermore, faulting modifies the arrangement of the materials in the crust, so that rocks of different hardness may be in contact with each other.

The fault plane along which slippage occurs may vary in orientation from vertical to horizontal and the direction of motion may be vertical, inclined, or horizontal. When the motion is primarily in the horizontal direction with very little vertical component a so-called strike-slip fault results. Such fault planes are generally vertical or nearly so. When the motion along a fault plane is either up or down, normal and reverse faults occur. Normal faults, which are generally steep, result when a part of the crust is in tension, perhaps associated with the bulging of a domal structure where the near surface rocks have been pushed upward from underneath and they must cover more distance than they did before. Reverse or thrust faults have a gentle dip and may in places be horizontal. They result from compression, where parts of the crust are horizontally squeezed together and one part rides up on top of another. Such faults are often associated with folding. When rocks start to be deformed by compression they may initially fold and then if the crumpling becomes too intense or too rapid, the rock mass may eventually yield by faulting.

The best-known strike-slip fault in the United States is the San

Andreas Fault in California, which extends from the desert area somewhat east of Los Angeles to the coast north of San Francisco. The rocks west of this fracture have moved northward with respect to those on the east side. Currently, there is a twisting of the crust here which is moving the rocks approximately two inches per year. Eventually the buildup of stress on the fault plane, due to this twisting of the land, will become too much and the rocks will suddenly slip, and an earthquake will be reported. The actual total amount of motion along the San Andreas Fault is a little hard to determine, but many geologists believe that there has been a slippage of up to 120 miles since the Cretaceous, and perhaps 350 miles since the Jurassic. This fault forms a line of weakness which has determined the location of river-cut valleys and lowland areas. It is marked at the northern end by Bolinas Lagoon, Tomales Bay, and Bodega Bay, and farther south in the San Francisco area by San Andreas Lake and Lower Crystal Springs Reservoir. The fault very obviously has formed a zone of weakness more easily weathered and eroded than the material on either side.

Another well-known example of a strike-slip fault is that of the Great Glen in Scotland. This fault cuts across the land northeast to southwest, and forms another zone of weakness, in this case leading to the erosion of a series of linear lakes and valleys, Loch Ness being one of them. In this fault the northern side moved southwest with respect to the southern side. In both these examples the same fault zone has been reactivated under later stresses and used again and again. In fact large structural elements in the crust representing either weak or strong zones will always influence, to some extent at least, the location of later geologic events.

In addition to joints, faults, domes, and folds, excellent evidence for former crustal unrest is given by unconformities. These are erosion surfaces which separate two masses of rock. A common type shows an angular relationship between an older tilted or folded sequence of layered rocks and a newer sequence of bedded rocks, generally sedimentary, deposited thereon. The evidence for instability lies in the fact that erosion must have occurred after a certain rock mass was formed and then conditions changed, so that new material could be deposited thereon. In other words, rocks were produced, uplifted, eroded, and then downwarping occurred so that new deposition could take place.

Two classic unconformities can be seen on the walls of the Grand Canyon. Near the bottom below the horizontal layers of the plateau proper, there is a sequence of tilted sedimentary rocks, which in turn overlies a mass of schist intruded by granite. Unconformities separate the tilted series from the underlying material, and the horizontal sediments from the tilted sequence. The history shown here started with the intrusion of the granite into the schist at great depth. Then in order to expose these rocks so that they could be covered by sediments the region must have been uplifted and deeply eroded, by the removal of millions upon millions of tons of material. The first sequence of now tilted sediments was deposited on this erosion surface. These in turn were uplifted, tilted, and then eroded, to be subsequently downwarped for the horizontal sequence to be deposited. The incision of the Colorado River into these various rock groups necessitates a still more recent time of uplift and erosion.

On the west flank of the Bighorn Mountains in Wyoming, Shell Canyon has been incised deeply and has cut through a tilted sequence of sediments which overlies granite. The granite is marked with well-developed vertical and horizontal joint systems, and lying directly on it is a layer of sandstone which is composed of minerals that were weathered and broken off from the granite. Obviously here the igneous rock after its cooling at great depth was uncovered by erosion and then the process reversed and sediments were piled on top of the eroded granite, thus forming an unconformable surface. More recently the crust has been subject to more diastrophism and erosion so that such evidence for past crustal motions have been exposed to view.

The United States can be divided into physiographic provinces, each one of which possesses a major structure differentiating it from the others, whether it be horizontal layers, folded, or faulted parts of the crust. For each one of these provinces the landscape features are more or less the same, because the structure is similar throughout. For instance, if we look at either the Colorado or Columbia Plateaus we can note that the scenery consists of mesas, cliffs, and benches. In both areas a sequence of horizontal layered rocks have been cut into by rivers. In the Colorado Plateau sedimentary rocks are present, and in the Columbia Plateau lava flows. The plains type of scenery develops where the rock layers are also horizontal, but the relief here is much less than in plateau regions. Folded mountain areas have their own major scenic features, such as parallel ridges and valleys, and faulted blocks of the crust have their characteristic look. The major differences between one physiographic province and another depends, first, on the structure present and, second, on the kind and age of the rocks, and the amount of erosion.

The major area of high relief in continental United States, ex-

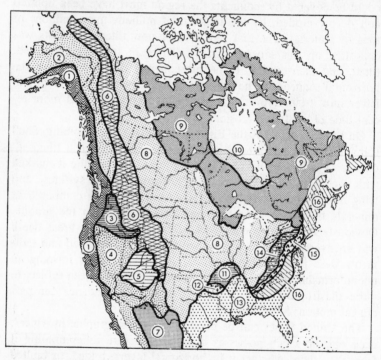

1. Pacific Mountain System
  Aleutians
  Coast Ranges
  Cascades
  Sierra Nevada
	5. Colorado Plateau	12. Ouachita Mountains

	6. Rocky Mountain System	13. Coastal Plain
	7. Mexican Highland	14. Appalachian Plateau
	8. Interior Plains	15. Appalachian Valley and Ridge Province
2. Intermontane Plateaus	9. Laurentian Upland	16. Piedmont, Blue Ridge, New England Province
3. Columbia Plateau	10. Hudson Bay Lowland	
4. Basin and Range Province	11. Ozark Plateau	

Physiographic provinces of North America

clusive of Alaska, lies in the western third, from the Rocky Mountains to the Pacific coast. The relatively flat Interior Lowlands cover the central areas and the Appalachian Province, a subdued mountainous tract compared with the western areas, with its bordering Atlantic Coastal Plain, complete the over-all picture.

The core of the continent, the Canadian Shield, is a deeply eroded area composed of old, highly contorted rocks, Precambrian in age, which have been intruded a number of times with granites. This area lies primarily outside the United States but extends into northern Michigan and Wisconsin, and northeastern Minnesota, and has an isolated extension which appears as the Adirondack Mountains of New York State. Elsewhere in the country limited areas of rocks of similar ancient age are visible, as at the Grand Canyon where all the materials under the horizontal sediments are Precambrian, and in various mountain ranges where uplift has promoted erosion to such an extent that the old rocks have been uncovered.

The Shield area is composed of exactly the same kind of materials as found elsewhere, lava flows, sediments, which have now been largely metamorphosed, granites, and other intrusives. They, of course, bear witness to the fact that volcanoes erupted, rocks were weathered, and sediments were laid down in the Precambrian much as they are now.

The Appalachian Province is divisible into three parts. The Older Appalachians, composed of the Piedmont, Blue Ridge, and New England areas, lie on the east. Then come the newer, Folded Appalachians, and lastly the Appalachian Plateau still farther to the west, completing the triumvirate.

The Atlantic and Gulf Coastal Plains are composed of sedimentary materials with a very slight seaward tilt to the layers. Their age varies from Cretaceous to modern. On their inland margin, on the west they overlap and cover the eroded parts of the Older Appalachians, and at the south the Folded Appalachians, while in the Gulf area they overlap the Interior Lowland rocks. These sediments if removed would uncover a greatly extended Interior Lowland and Appalachian Province.

The isolated Ozark and Ouachita Mountains in the central part of the country perhaps represent a continuation of the Appalachian Plateau in the Ozarks and the Folded Appalachians in the Ouachita, which have been separated by the Coastal Plain cover in between.

In the Western Cordillera, the Rocky Mountains lie at the east, and the Sierra Nevada, Cascades, and Coast Ranges on the west. Between these two major mountain masses the Columbia Plateau lies at the north, the Basin and Range Province in the center, and the Colorado Plateau at the south. As noted the rock layers are essentially horizontal in both plain and plateau areas, but the uplift in the plateaus has been much more with the result that rivers have been able to cut deep canyons, thus giving a greater relief.

The Basin and Range is an area of many fault block mountains, and the Sierra Nevada is a large block of the crust which has been uplifted along a major fault at the east and tilted slightly toward the west. The Cascades consist of a series of strato-volcanoes which extend from northern California into Canada. The Coast Ranges are relatively complex, faulted and folded mountains, separated from the Sierra Nevadas by the Central Valley of California, which averages about 50 miles in width and is 400 miles long, north to south. Still farther north, the Coast Ranges are separated from the Cascades by the Willamette Valley and the Puget Sound Lowland. The Western Cordillera is thus seen to comprise a number of diverse types of structure with resulting variations in scenery.

The western series of physiographic provinces as developed in the United States continue north through Canada, and thence northwest into Alaska. The structure, general age of the rocks, and geologic history of the Alaskan Provinces are similar to those farther south. The Coastal Mountain System of Alaska is the continuation of the United States and British Columbia Coast Ranges. The Aleutians, a 1,600-mile arc with 80 volcanoes, 47 of them active, marks the continuation of the very active volcanic zone which is represented in the United States by the Cascade Mountains. The interior hills and valleys of Alaska are a continuation of the Columbia Plateau and intermontane valleys of British Columbia. The Brooks Range which lies in the northern part of Alaska belongs to the United States and Canadian Rocky Mountain system, and the Arctic Coastal Plain north of the Brooks Range is structurally a continuation of the Interior Plains from farther south.

To summarize, the plains whether they be coastal or interior are areas of low relief underlain by horizontal layers, sedimentary in almost all cases. The rocks even here, however, may be slightly deformed into gentle domes and basins, where the inclination of the layers is so little that it is hardly noticeable. Not many feet in elevation exist between the highest and lowest parts of any region in the plains. Plateaus, on the other hand, are regions of high relief, underlain again by essentially horizontal rocks. The relief is such that it may be thousands of feet deep. In mountain areas, the relief is also large, but the underlying material has generally been contorted into folds, or faulted structures.

The major physiographic divisions of the land can be subdivided into smaller units, on various types of criteria, such as the amount and kind of vegetation cover, and the extent and type of erosion. For instance, in the Colorado Plateau the higher areas are well watered with large stands of trees, and the lower parts are deserts. Some parts are well dissected with intersecting canyons and ramifying gullies. Other parts are flat for long distances, with little close dissection. Such diversity of scenery might tend to distract the observer from the main theme, but underlying all parts is the basic horizontal structure of the rocks, which controls the permissible variety of landforms that can be produced.

(Litton Industries-Aero Service Division)

The plains near Morley, Iowa

CHAPTER XII

THE PLAINS

The plains of the United States occupy two major areas, the Atlantic to Gulf coast region and the interior parts of the country from the Appalachian to the Rocky Mountains. In both these regions the land is generally flat with low hills left between shallow river-cut valleys. The bedrock underlying the surface is composed essentially of horizontal sedimentary layers, some of which are largely unconsolidated as in the more recently formed Coastal Plain, and others well consolidated into sedimentary rocks, especially in the eastern parts of the Interior Lowlands.

The Atlantic Coastal Plain is bordered on its western margin by the older rocks of the Appalachian Piedmont. Because these rocks are more resistant to weathering and erosion than the Coastal Plain sediments, the rivers which cross this boundary often drop onto the softer material in a series of falls and rapids. The Fall Line thus divides the more sluggish, lower reaches of these rivers, which are often navigable, from the more rapid stretches in the Piedmont above.

The northern parts of the Atlantic Coastal Plain—Cape Cod, Long Island, and northern New Jersey—have been glaciated, and are therefore characterized by a variety of glacial features, such as moraines, outwash, and kettle holes. North of Cape Cod the Coastal Plain disappears under the ocean; the same structure and rocks are, however, present on the Continental Shelf. For instance, the fishing banks off Maine and Nova Scotia are parts of this drowned coastal plain, where there is relatively shallow water.

The age of the rocks composing the Atlantic and Gulf Coastal Plains varies from Cretaceous to Recent. The oldest layers outcrop at the inner margin of the Plain and the most recent near the ocean. The layers, which in general have a slight seaward tilt, will on erosion produce a series of cuestas, or asymmetric ridges with one steep side. Such erosional features are left wherever a slightly tilted resistant layer lies between softer rock. The overlying material is removed, leaving the resistant layer to cap the softer material beneath. On the Coastal Plain, since the sediments dip seaward, the steeper side of the cuesta faces inland and the gentle slope seaward. The cuestas here are marked often by a series of low hills which are most noticeable from the landward side.

The Coastal Plain and the Continental Shelf collectively are underlain by a very thick wedge of sediments which starts at the Piedmont, reaches a maximum thickness at approximately the coastline and tapers off at the Continental Slope. The Shelf and Plain are geologically similar, with the same structure and types of rock throughout. From the Cretaceous to the present the coastline has shifted from one extreme to the other, from the edge of the Piedmont to the top of the Slope.

The same general structure is found in the Gulf coast as along the Atlantic, but here the sediments are much thicker, reaching 30,000 to 40,000 feet near the Mississippi delta, where deposition has been rapid since the Cretaceous. Subsidence of the land in the New Orleans area is constantly occurring, the result probably of a combination of downwarping, compaction of the sediments, and variations in sea level. The major topographic features here are natural levees, thus emphasizing the importance of deposition rather than erosion.

The Gulf region is very important for the exploitation of oil and natural gas, which are found widely distributed in the more porous rock layers. Petroleum, a mixture of hydrocarbons, requires for its presence first of all a source rock, that is, a sediment in which organic material has been deposited, and which has changed to oil through some process as yet unknown. A porous reservoir rock in which the oil can accumulate, generally a sandstone or limestone, and a proper structure to trap the oil and gas are also necessary. Most oil, being lighter than water, will percolate upward through water-soaked sediments until it can go no farther, that is, until a cap of some impervious material such as shale is reached. The classic type of oil trap is an anticline, where the oil has moved up to the top of the structure into a sandstone or a limestone, overlain by shale. In such an ideal case the reservoir rock may have natural gas filling the pore spaces at the very top, underlying which is oil and underneath that, in turn, water. When a hole is drilled from the surface and reaches the top part of the anticline, gas emerges; if the hole taps the side of the structure oil will come out, and from farther down the side, water.

Initially the oil in a newly tapped field may be under such pressure that it squirts out at the surface as a "gusher." With time the pressure of gas which drives the oil out becomes less and eventually the oil must be pumped from the hole. However, even after all the oil possible has been pumped from the ground there is still a great deal left which had not flowed into the well openings. Such oil can be recovered by various techniques which entail pushing the oil out of the porous reservoir into the wells. This has been accomplished by flooding with water or gas, each under pressure. They are pumped into the ground through a series of wells and then drive the remaining oil into a second series of wells.

Petroleum has been found in many places in the United States, always associated with sedimentary rock. The Gulf coast and the Interior Plains areas have yielded many important oil fields, as have also the Rocky Mountain and California areas.

The first commercial oil well in the United States was drilled in Pennsylvania when Edwin L. Drake completed one on August 27, 1859, near Titusville. He struck oil at a depth of $69\frac{1}{2}$ feet from the surface. Since that time the production and use of oil have increased until they are measured in billions of barrels.

Very interesting features found on the Gulf coast are the salt domes. These are plugs of salt, typically about a mile in diameter, and 15,000 to 20,000 feet high. At least 150 of them have been found, some offshore. They are formed when a mass of sedimentary salt from a lower position squeezes up through overlying layers, pushing them into a domal structure and in so doing cutting off the upturned edges of the layers which it intrudes. In this way possible oil traps are formed, both in the overlying dome, which is similar to an anticline, and in the upturned cut-off layers, since the ends are plugged by the salt. Salt domes, in addition to those on the Gulf coast are found in a number of places in the world, notably near the Caspian Sea, the North German plains, and the Carpathians of Romania. In Iran, the salt has actually extruded onto the surface, but due to aridity has not been removed by solution.

Sulfur deposits are associated with some of the salt domes. They appear in the limestone cap which commonly lies on top of the salt. A well-known sulfur deposit is that of the Grand Isle Mine, which is located about seven miles offshore in Louisiana, in water about 50 feet deep. Here a salt dome cap, with 220 to 425 feet of sulfur-bearing limestone 1,800 to 2,500 feet under the surface, has been drilled. Water at 325 degrees F is forced into the ore, and the sulfur, which melts at 240 degrees F, flows downward to the bottom of the well from where it is piped, as a liquid, to the surface. The wells, drilled from a platform overlying the dome, radiate downward to the ore body. It is predicted that the floor of the Gulf here will eventually subside about 45 feet after the ore has been removed.

Structure similar to the Coastal Plain is found in the Interior Lowlands. The sedimentary rocks are to the first approximation horizontal, but from a regional standpoint, are found to dip gently. However, unlike the Coastal Plain where the dip is seaward, the layers may dip in various directions, the result of gentle warping into basins and domes. The tilt of the layers is generally too slight to be noticeable at any one place, often being much less than one degree, but when the same layer is traced across country it may be found to change level by some tens of feet per mile.

The land on the whole is generally flat with occasional gently rolling hills. There are two basic scenic elements here, subject to many modifications, the cuesta ridge which may extend for very long distances, and the river valley with its bordering zone of often highly dissected bluffs. The bluffs and zones of low hills are constantly being destroyed. The valley floors have thus become wider and wider with time, as the sides retreat away from the river. River

valleys in the plains will never be very deep. There are no rushing
streams or deep gorges here; rivers meander with a gentle flow.
They start at too low an elevation to cut deeply.

A typical series of river bluffs is located at Chamberlin, South
Dakota, where the Mississippi River has a narrow floodplain, now
covered by the Fort Randall Reservoir. As one leaves the river
here a wide belt of rather knobby grass-covered dissected land

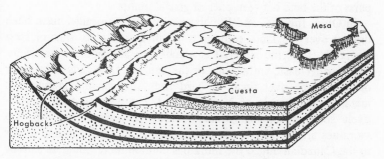

Mesa, cuesta, hogback: some basic erosional features associated
with layered rocks

must first be climbed before reaching the flat upland of the plains.
The rise totals a few hundred feet in a few miles. The ramifying
side valleys which are cut into the bluff zone grow rapidly shal-
lower and come to an end in the flat plain above. In the case of
rivers with wider floodplains the line of bluffs and dissected country may start well away from the river.

The northern parts of the Interior Lowlands, as well as the
Coastal Plain, have been greatly modified by glaciers, which have
dumped moraines, drumlins, erratics, and a variety of assorted
material onto the underlying rocks, essentially smothering the preglacial scenery. These deposits now form the major features of the
land except where some of the larger cuesta ridges, such as the
Niagara cuesta, protrude through the glacial cover. This is quite
unlike the situation in New England where the glacier came down
into a rather hilly area, and produced U-shaped valleys, concen-
trating its deposition in the lower parts of the region.

Glaciated country is noted for its lakes and swamps. The heterogeneous dumping of glacial debris has disturbed and often entirely destroyed the lines of preglacial drainage and has in many cases forced rivers to take entirely new paths. The northern Mississippi River is a stream whose path has been almost entirely determined by glacial action. After each advance of the ice much of the river was forced into a different course. Now, for long stretches the upper Mississippi River has poorly defined walls. The river has not cut its valley here, but wanders through the lower parts of the land between piles of glacial dump.

In Ohio, Indiana, and Illinois, a number of moraines have been draped over the land, composed of till quite unlike that of New England. Here, the material is much finer and boulders, so common farther east, are absent. In the Interior Lowlands the glacier did not come over areas of hard rock such as the granite and metamorphic terrain of New England, but over an area of relatively softer sediments, which it easily pulverized, and thus the moraines are far less stony. Farther north, in Michigan and closer to the Canadian Shield the moraines contain more boulders as they are nearer to areas of igneous and metamorphic rocks.

One of the most notable drumlin fields in the country is located in the eastern part of the Interior Lowlands. Between Lake Ontario and the northern margin of the Appalachian Plateau in the vicinity of Rochester, New York, the drumlins were plastered onto the land by the southward-moving ice. These drumlin fields can best be observed from the air; an aerial photograph clearly reveals the remarkable regularity of shape and alignment of the numerous small hills to a degree unobtainable by an observer on the ground.

The contrast between glaciated and unglaciated land is often very marked. For example, a region of about 15,000 square miles lying primarily in Wisconsin but with a narrow wedge in northern Illinois was never covered by the continental glacier in any of its four major advances. The area all around it, however, was covered by one or another of the advances. This Driftless Area has a distinctive type of scenery quite unlike that of the glaciated country around it, and of course resembles the unglaciated land farther south. There are many erosional remnants, ridges, buttes, and delicate rock pillars which would have been quickly destroyed by any overriding ice. A mass of resistant rocks in northern Wisconsin formed an area of highlands which protected the area of the south. Furthermore, the lowlands of Lake Superior and Lake Michigan formed channels for the easy passage of ice around this bastion; thus the Driftless Area was preserved.

Some of the flattest parts of the land are not erosion surfaces but surfaces of deposition, such as river floodplains, and abandoned lake floors. For instance, at Grand Forks, North Dakota, the land is so flat that one looks in vain as far as the horizon for the slightest perceptible undulation of the surface. Here we are on the floor of a now-vanished glacial lake, Lake Agassiz. This lake, at one time larger than all the present Great Lakes combined, came into existence when the river which drained the area toward the north was dammed in its northern reaches by the retreating Canadian ice sheet. And it disappeared when the continental sheet finally melted away. An arm of Lake Agassiz extended into the United States to cover the present Minnesota-North Dakota boundary line. This section was about 150 miles long, north to south, and about 80 miles wide. In Canada the lake expanded into its major portion, to include the Lake of the Woods, Lake Winnipeg, and a number of other present-day lakes.

The Great Lakes also were at times larger and spilled over onto adjoining country during the Ice Age. The presence of such enlargements is indicated by the flat land which now fringes many of the lakes. Chicago is built on the floor of an extended Lake Michigan, and Detroit on the floor of an extended Lake Erie.

Drained lake floors are very flat but if a sufficiently large area is studied they are found to have a slight regional slope, down which rivers will flow in roughly parallel courses. Such a situation is easily noted on a detailed map of the Fargo, North Dakota, area. Similarly, the Coastal Plain had a gentle regional dip seaward and rivers flowing down across this slope did so in courses parallel to each other, and at right angles to the shoreline.

The North American continental glacier had a number of indirect effects in country it did not actually cover. As we have seen, the loess in the Central Plains originated as glacial outwash from which the wind derived the dust now found in these deposits.

Another indirect effect of the glaciers is found in the Gulf area where the Mississippi River went through a number of stages. First

it carried enormous quantities of meltwater from the receding glaciers along with large quantities of sediments which were dumped
in the delta. As the ice melted the ocean rose and normally would
have flooded into the lower Mississippi valley. However, the river
carried such large quantities of debris that delta-building has more
than kept up with any incipient estuary.

Where the plains are arid to semiarid a badland type of topography may develop along river bluffs. An excellent example of this
is the Badlands of South Dakota. Here the White River has cut
hundreds of feet into a sequence of sediments, composed largely of
fine clay with a few thin sandstone beds and other more resistant
parts. The glowing white bare slopes have retreated in complicated
gullies which are intricately dissected, and very close to each other.
Erosion is so rapid that vegetation has little chance to get started
on the steep slopes, whereas the flat areas, a number of separate
levels being obvious, are covered with grass and low vegetation.
Such badland topography develops where rock layers are soft,
easily eroded, and distinctly above the level of a major stream
which drains the region.

Erosion in the South Dakota Badlands and in the continental
deposits elsewhere along the front of the Rocky Mountains has
brought to view the fossil remains of many animals which lived in
the Tertiary when these deposits were being laid down. There were
a great variety of small horses, camels, and rhinoceros which lived
and grazed in this formerly well-watered area, where carnivores,
such as tigers and wild dogs, lived on the rich game.

Many of the scenic forms in the plains can best be appreciated
from the air or from a map which gives the over-all relationships
of hills and slopes and drainage patterns. Drainage patterns here
are dendritic, that is, a major stream with its tributaries and subtributaries resembles the trunk of a tree with its branches and twigs.
Such a pattern develops when rocks are homogeneous in their
resistance to erosion. In such cases no one stream will cut more
rapidly downward than its neighbor; all have the same type and
resistance of material over which they flow, and into which they
incise their courses.

The map or air viewpoint is also necessary to appreciate how
cuesta ridges encircle both dome and basin structures, which may

be many tens of miles across, such as the Michigan Basin with its encircling steep scarps facing outward from the center. The structure here is analogous to a series of plates stacked one on top of the other. Erosion has removed more of the outer parts of the topmost plate, and has removed less of each succeeding lower-lying plate. The Niagara River at the falls descends over a limestone cuesta which, farther west, partly encircles the Michigan Basin. As the falls retreat the elevation of the cap rock will become less and less until eventually the falls as such will disappear. The erosion of a sequence of domed layers develops a series of cuesta ridges whose steep scarp, unlike the basin, face inward toward the center of the structure, such as those surrounding the uplifted Cincinnati-Nashville area.

A cuesta ridge, as we have seen, results from the erosion of layered rocks with a gentle tilt where one of the layers is slightly more resistant than the material above and below it. The hogback ridge has a similar origin but the dip of the rocks is greater, so that the slope on one side of the ridge is essentially the same as that on the other. Many hogback ridges fringe the Rocky Mountains on the east where the rocks of the plains have been upturned, some of them vertically, at the time that the Rockies were folded, and now the tattered ends of the more resistant layers protrude as ridges. In contrast, if there is no dip to the layers and a more resistant rock overlies a less resistant one, we have a cliff with a slope underneath, and if such a structure has been isolated by erosion a mesa will result.

The geologic history of the Interior Plains has been a relatively quiet one since the beginning of the Paleozoic Era, about 500 million years ago. During much of the Paleozoic and Mesozoic Eras seas came and went and spread alternating layers of lime, mud, and sand, now turned into limestone, shale, and sandstone. The Rockies were folded at the end of the Mesozoic Era. Subsequently they were worn down and debris from them formed widespread coalescing alluvial fans and floodplain deposits which created a wedge of sediments some hundreds of miles wide, covering the western edge of the plains. More recently, at the end of the Tertiary the Rockies were elevated again. Active weathering and erosion was thus initiated, especially in the mountains, but also in the nearby sediments of the plains. Such a history explains the relatively greater dissection of the plains near Denver, which changes to less highly eroded country eastward, in western Kansas and northern Texas. Still farther east beyond the extent of the Tertiary continental sediments the rocks are older, generally Paleozoic and Mesozoic in age, and in this area fossils of older types of marine life especially have been uncovered. For instance, in Kansas, remains of Mesozoic marine reptiles such as the long-necked plesiosaur and the fishlike ichthyosaur have been found. Both these forms became extinct at the end of the Mesozoic.

The most recent geological event to affect the plains area was the coming of the glacier and the spreading of thick masses of debris in the northern parts, with indirect effects due to climatic and sea-level changes elsewhere. The whole region now is one of essentially low relief, undramatic in most areas with the exception of such isolated features as the Badlands. Those who understand its history will find it interesting, but many are apt to traverse it quickly on the way to the more dramatic scenery in the plateau and mountain country farther west.

CHAPTER XIII

PLATEAUS

The Appalachian, Columbia, and Colorado Plateaus are the three large areas in the United States lying at a relatively high elevation, in which layered rocks are essentially horizontal and the relief is measured in many hundreds to thousands of feet. In places, where the valleys are widely spaced, extensive uneroded flat areas exist, and in others the cutting of canyons and valleys has been so universal that there are comparatively few flat sections left. An even skyline, flat mesas, and the arrangement of the rocks as seen on cliff faces and canyon walls, all reflect this basic horizontal structure. Any valley cut into such a sequence must intersect a variety of materials, some resistant, as sandstone and limestone, and others weak, such as shale. Thus any typical valley has walls which do not descend uniformly to the river, but consist of steep and gentle slopes alternately, the cliffs occurring where the layers are strong and can stand up without crumbling and the slopes where material is less able to stand by itself.

The Colorado Plateau Province affords an excellent and classic example of plateau scenery developed under arid to semiarid conditions. This very colorful region covers over 130,000 square miles, lying primarily in southern Utah and northern Arizona, but with appreciable portions in northwestern New Mexico and southwestern Colorado. The rocks of the area are primarily sedimentary, laid down on a Precambrian foundation and now forming a

(John Shimer)

thick sequence, thousands of feet in depth. Sedimentation in at least parts of the area continued throughout the Paleozoic, Mesozoic, and Cenozoic Eras. Most of the sediments, as shown by their contained fossils, were deposited in the sea which inundated the area at various times. The general elevation of the region outside the deeper canyon floors is over 5,000 feet with parts rising more than 11,000 feet above sea level. At the higher elevations the rainfall is heavy and pine forests are found, whereas in the lower areas the rainfall is so slight that arid lands such as the Painted Desert prevail.

The same basic horizontal structure is obvious everywhere in the Colorado Plateau. A great diversity of detailed scenic elements, has been formed by weathering and erosion working on materials of varying resistance. An over-all dendritic drainage pattern is present, with angular interesections, however, at many tributary junctions, owing to the well-developed systems of vertical joints which determine the junctions between cliff faces and the locations of the tributaries to some extent.

The Colorado River at the Grand Canyon has cut through the horizontal sediments to uncover the Precambrian basement at the bottom; thus it affords a superlative cross-sectional view of the rocks of the plateau.

The north side of the Canyon is about 12 miles away from the south side and is approximately 1,200 feet higher. This higher elevation has caused a greater precipitation and the development of a forest, whereas on the south side there is only a scrubby semiarid type of vegetation. Back of both rims the land is flat and largely ungullied. From the top of the canyon walls the river, about one mile down, appears as a thin insignificant thread of water. It has been responsible, however, for the removal of all the material which is now missing between the two rims. After having been broken up by the physical and chemical processes of weathering, the material was washed, fell, or slid down the valley slopes. Then, after reaching the river, such debris was promptly washed out of the area by the rapidly moving water, and in the process acted as an abrasive to scour the bedrock of the river channel yet deeper. As the river moves down toward the sea it carries an immense load of mud, sand, and gravel, some of it in suspension, and much of it

The Colorado Plateau and River
near Deadhorse Point, Utah

as a bed load rolling and scraping along the bottom. The load is so large that the river is brown in color from the suspended mud and fine sand, quite different from the clear tributaries which can be seen joining it here and there, such as Bright Angel Creek. At the present time this load, instead of being carried into the sea, is trapped behind Boulder Dam and is rapidly filling Lake Mead.

From a regional standpoint the plateau rocks at the Grand Canyon were uplifted to form a broad arch, which dips very gently both southward and northward from the canyon area. Because of this up-arched structure more material has been removed, and older rocks uncovered at the canyon than elsewhere in the Plateau. Here the youngest rocks present are Permian in age, and form the topmost layers of the canyon, whereas at the bottom the river has uncovered the Precambrian basement. The edge view of about a mile of Paleozoic sediments is thus exposed. As one goes northward from the canyon younger and younger material is traversed because the slight regional tilt in that direction has resulted in less erosion compared with the more uplifted parts to the south. Each time a resistant layer is encountered it will form a cliff facing south with a gentle dip slope northward. On a trip north three major cliffs must be surmounted and each time one is climbed we go down a gentle slope to find a new cliff formed of a younger resistant layer barring the way. The Vermilion, White, and Pink Cliffs are climbed in this fashion. Each cliff line marks the steep scarp of a cuesta, in this case the edge of a layer which is being peeled off the land, and which has already been removed from the area farther south.

A white, massive sandstone forms the White Cliffs, the material into which Zion Canyon has been cut. There are very few breaks in the walls which surround this valley. The sandstone is massive with widely spaced joint cracks, and the influence of stratification on the details of the canyon walls is not marked because of the uniformity of the rock. Particularly fine examples of large-scale cross-bedding in the massive sandstone cliffs are to be seen here at Zion Canyon.

The Pink Cliffs, formed of the youngest or topmost layer, are found at Bryce Canyon. Here a very irregular cliff face is composed of poorly consolidated shales with a few interbedded limy

and sandy layers. The irregular retreat of the cliff and the fine
gullying resembles the situation to be found in the Badlands area
of South Dakota. Bryce Canyon with its slender pinnacles etched
from the brightly colored sedimentary layers clearly shows the
selective removal of certain portions of the rock at the expense of
others. The influence of horizontal layering can be noted on the

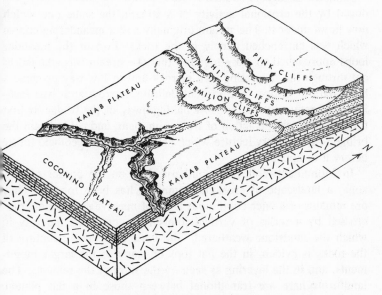

Generalized diagram of the Colorado Plateau
near the Grand Canyon

sides of the vertical pinnacles, where color changes reflect the
alternating more and less resistant layers. A number of the pillars
are capped by a small remnant of slightly harder rock which has
protected the more easily crumbled layers beneath.

In the Arches National Monument near Moab a number of
natural bridges have been etched into a massive sandstone. Here a
series of vertical master joints spaced about 20 feet apart has led
to the isolation of finlike masses of sandstone approximately 20
feet across, 100 feet or more in height, and some hundreds to

thousands of feet long. After these stone blocks were thus fashioned a delicate etching process formed windows through the fins
to give arches of stone. Such quarrying was due largely to water
which entered small cracks in the rock and removed the cement
holding the grains together. Once produced, the arches will continue to get smaller and thinner, and eventually of course will
disappear.

Rainbow Bridge in southern Utah, unlike the arches, was produced by the erosional activity of a stream, the same one which
now flows under it. The stream originally had a meandering course
which was entrenched deeply in the rocks. Two of the meander
loops approached so close together that the stream was enabled to
cut through the separating wall of rock and in this way produce a
thick natural bridge. The present delicate, narrow arch was fashioned subsequently by the slow flaking away of the bridge as first
formed, through the action of frost, rain, heat, and cold. Again the
bridge is a transitory feature which has a very short geologic future
before it disappears.

In Monument Valley, in southern Utah on the border of Arizona, a landscape of erosional remnants has been formed. They
are remains of a once continuous layer of massive sandstone, criss-
crossed by a series of vertical joints that controlled the way in
which the sandstone weathered. The basic horizontal structure of
the rocks is evident in the flat tops of many of the larger monu-
ments, and in the layering as seen on the sides of the remains. The
landforms here are transitional between those in a flat plateau
upland trenched by a few widely spaced canyons and a flat lowland
area with only a few isolated remnants remaining. Such a low-lying
flat surface marks the inevitable end of a cycle of erosion, initiated
by the uplift of land with respect to sea level.

Although the general structure of any plateau area is horizontal,
in a number of places, the rocks may have enough of a dip so that
cuestas can be formed. That at Mesa Verde is classic. Here a
resistant layer of sandstone, sandwiched between softer layers, is
tilted slightly southward. Erosion has uncovered the sandstone and
removed its uptilted end to a northward-facing scarp. Streams
flowing southward along the dip slope have cut a series of parallel
canyons which are in the process of destroying the tilted "mesa."

In a number of places the cap rock has been slightly undercut so that shallow caves have been formed, in which there are well-preserved Indian cliff dwellings.

Relatively recently volcanic activity·has occurred to modify the basic features of the Colorado Plateau. Here and there cinder cones dot the surface, such as Sunset Crater south of the Grand Canyon and, where the volcanic activity has been dormant for some time, volcanic necks have been etched out, such as that at Ship Rock in northwestern New Mexico.

The interest and dramatic appeal of the Colorado Plateau lies in the tattered and sculptured look of the land, where various essentially horizontal layers differing in resistance and color, one from another, have been eroded to produce many modifications of the basic simple cliff face and slope. A vertical system of jointing has formed other planes of weakness, which in places have played a dominant role in controlling the way in which the rocks have yielded to the forces of weathering and erosion and has locally determined the arrangement of river channels and cliff faces. With time the future of the Plateau is inevitable. It will be worn down to a more or less flat, featureless plain if the forces of diastrophism do not in the meantime push the area up again.

The Columbia Plateau is distinct from the Colorado. It is composed of many layers of lava, collectively thousands of feet thick, generally of dark-colored basalts but with lighter-colored flows, reds, and purples in a few places. The flows were extruded in the Cenozoic Era, some so recently that the landscape appears as if they had just been formed. The volcanic area on the whole extends for over 100,000 square miles from the Grand Tetons of Wyoming on the east to the Cascade Mountains of Oregon and Washington on the west. On the south it is bordered by the Basin and Range Province and on the east and the north by the Rockies.

The plateau type of scenery is obvious here, especially where rivers have cut through the older layers thus giving a cross-sectional view of former flows. Flat surfaces, vertical cliffs where the lava is more resistant, slopes where interbedded softer sediments or more easily eroded layers of lava occur are basic elements of the scenery. The individual sheets of lava vary in thickness from 10 to 200 feet, and on recently cut canyon walls as many as 20 layers have been counted in a single exposure. The width of the average fissure from which the lava emerged was probably rarely more than a few feet. As we have seen, eroded exposures of similar feeding cracks on Hawaii, now filled with frozen lava to a depth of over 4,000 feet, show they are narrow and do not widen appreciably with depth.

The accumulation of the rocks began about 50 million years ago in the Eocene Epoch, when flows started to engulf a region with a relief of probably 2,000 to 3,000 feet, and has lasted intermittently up to recent times. The climax of the volcanic activity was at the end of the Miocene. During the Pliocene and the Pleistocene the high strato-volcanoes of the Cascades on the western margin of the plateau area were built up, and there was great volcanic activity in the Snake River Plain in southern Idaho.

Between individual flows a soil was often developed before another time of volcanism occurred. Furthermore, flows often disrupted the preflow lines of drainage so that lakes were formed, which were then filled with sediments. Thus, interbedded with the lava flows are soils and sediments, some of the latter forming important aquifers. The crust here was not stable from the Eocene to the present but was shaken by intermittent diastrophism. Thus on visiting this area one can see the earlier flows broken and disrupted by later times of crustal instability.

In the eastern part of the United States the Appalachian Plateau is distinct from the other two, at least in its superficial aspect. This area, bordered by the Folded Appalachian Mountains on the east, and by the Interior Lowlands on the west, is one of Paleozoic sediments which have been uplifted and extensively weathered and eroded in a humid climate. The slopes are rounded and the layered structure of the bedrock is less obvious than in the plateau areas of the west. The alternating cliff face and slope in the Appalachian area has been rounded by the greater chemical weathering and smoothed over by soil and vegetation. Furthermore, the amount of dissection has in general been greater so that there are relatively few flat elevated areas undissected by stream erosion, such as are so common in the west.

CHAPTER XIV

MOUNTAINS

Mountains do not occur as isolated lonely peaks scattered at random over the face of the earth, but in ranges, chains, and systems, representing structures with a common age and history. This is well illustrated in the United States where the two major mountainous areas which lie in the western and eastern thirds of the country are each composed of linear groups of mountains. The Western Cordillera, which includes the Rocky Mountains and all the intervening territory to the Pacific coast, is extensive and rugged, while the Appalachian Highlands in the east are confined to a smaller region and are more subdued in aspect.

A mountain is an elevated area of limited extent, the home of bare rock ledges, landslides, and rapid streams. The angle of slope in many places is so great that any soil cover is removed essentially as fast as it is formed. It is here that the structure of the materials of the crust is often visible in the form of faults, folds, and joints; and the interplay between the destructive activities associated with weathering and erosion and the constructive aspects of igneous activity and disastrophism, which produces folded and fault block mountains, are most obvious. Widespread areas of metamorphic rocks as well as granite should be expected in the cores of mountain ranges where there has been most uplift and thus greatest erosion.

A number of mountain chains, such as the Appalachians, the

(Geological Survey of Canada)

Rocky Mountains near Windermere, British Columbia

Rockies, the Alps, and the Himalayas, are carved out of very thick and extensive sequences of sedimentary rocks. The layers are found in every conceivable orientation—horizontal, tilted, vertical, closely crumpled, or displaced by faults. Obviously, after the accumulation of a thick pile of sediments such areas were subject to intense diastrophic action, folding and faulting, which was accompanied by a significant shortening of the crust.

If the folded rocks of any of these mountains are straightened out in imagination, they will cover in the unfolded, initial position a far wider area than they do now in their crumpled and contorted state. For example, the Applachian Ridge and Valley section has been subject to approximately a 30 per cent shortening in the northwest to southeast direction. Rock layers which formerly extended for three miles now cover only two. The percentage of shortening in the Alps, which at one time extended much farther in the north to south direction than they do now, has been estimated to be 65 per cent according to some authorities and as much as 76 per cent by others. The structure is so complex that it is very difficult to calculate the original extent of the layers.

James Hall (1811–1898), a New York State geologist, noted the very thick sequences of rocks in the Appalachian Mountains compared with other areas in the United States. In 1859, the same year that Darwin's *Origin of Species* appeared, he proposed that the crust bowed down under the load of accumulating sediments and that in this way the thick mass was produced. His ideas were published in a large monograph on the Appalachian Mountains dealing especially with New York State. James Dwight Dana (1813–1895) subsequently coined the term "geosynclinal" for the trough into which these sediments were laid, and postulated the necessary rise of a neighboring area, which he called "geanticline," as the geosyncline sank. A balance here was thus suggested; the geanticline was thought to rise about as rapidly as the weathered parts of it were washed into the sinking geosyncline.

If there is a place available for sediments to accumulate, such as a geosyncline, they will do so very rapidly, and throughout geologic history a fantastic quantity of material has been dumped by the agents of erosion, first in one place and then in another. Altogether more than 70 miles of sediments has been deposited in the last 600 million years, that is, since the beginning of the Cambrian. However, it is vital to bear in mind that no one place in the world has received this thickness of sediments. The areas which were downwarped and received sediments have kept shifting from one place on the earth's surface to another throughout geologic time, and the cumulative thickness is obtained by adding the maximum thicknesses found in one area to layers deposited subsequently in another, as demonstrated by fossil correlation.

The Appalachian Mountains afford an excellent example of a fold mountain range whose history consists of the typical three parts, rock-making, mountain-making, and lastly, mountain-carving. The rocks were deposited in the Appalachian geosyncline, which extended for over 1,500 miles from Canada to the Gulf of Mexico, and had a varying width of 300 to 400 miles. It existed as a subsiding lowland area throughout the Paleozoic Era, for approximately 300 million years. Most of the material deposited therein was washed down from the highlands which lay to the east, approximately where the present Coastal Plain now lies. This enormously thick wedge of sediments, one layer piled on another, and seven miles thick in places, formed the raw materials from which the present Appalachian Mountains are carved.

The Appalachian geosynclinal history itself consisted of two stages. The sediments in the eastern part of the geosyncline, that is, toward the Atlantic Ocean, were folded, metamorphosed, and intruded by magma in relatively early Paleozoic orogenies, the important one being in late Ordovician. These materials are now found in the New England, Piedmont, and Blue Ridge areas. Much of the western or inner part, toward the continent, was folded and faulted in the late Paleozoic and now forms the Folded Ridge and Valley section of the Appalachians, with the largely undeformed Appalachian Plateau rocks farther west.

The Ridge and Valley section with its bordering Plateau area extends over 1,000 miles from New York State to northern Alabama. In Pennsylvania the range of folded mountains is about 80 miles wide, and farther south 30 to 40 miles. Northward in the Hudson valley lowland of New York State it is narrower still, about 20 miles wide. Any area of folded rocks is characterized by hogback ridges and intervening valleys, roughly parallel with the

Development of the folded Appalachian Mountains

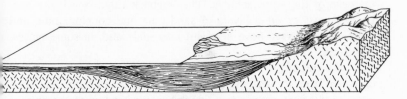

Deposition in the Paleozoic geosyncline

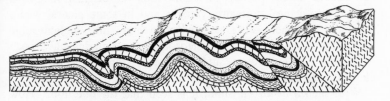

Folding and faulting at the end of the Paleozoic

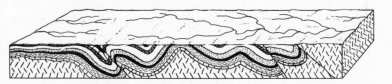

Peneplanation

Present-day ridges and valleys resulting from uplift and renewed erosion.

(From *This Sculptured Earth* by John A. Shimer. Permission of Columbia University Press)

major axis of the mountain range, that is, northeast to southwest in the case of the Appalachians. The hogback ridges mark the protruding parts of tilted layers of sandstone and conglomerate, and the valleys between have been cut into shale and, in some places, limestone.

By the end of the Paleozoic the rocks of the Appalachian Mountains had been formed and a structure of folds and faults had been given to this part of the crust, which has persisted up to the present time, and which has continually controlled the location of ridges and valleys. In the process of deformation the original sediments were changed into sedimentary rocks and in some places, where pressures and heat were somewhat greater, into metamorphic rocks. Since the end of the Paleozoic the mountains have been worn down at least once, and the present mountains owe their elevation to a later general arching of the region.

With such a history in mind it is seen that the question, "How old is a mountain?" is not easy to answer. One· must qualify any reply. Three ages often are pertinent, the age of the rocks, the age of the initial folding and faulting which produced the structure, and the age of the most recent uplift which has inaugurated the last cycle of erosion.

The Appalachian Mountains are now being washed piecemeal back toward the east, roughly from where the material originally came. Historically, there was first a general planation of the area. The initial folded and faulted mountains, running northeast-southwest, were reduced to a flat, more or less featureless surface. A second stage of the postorogenic history was initiated by the deposition, on this erosion surface, of a layer of sediments which covered the underlying structure. This layer was a continuation of the coastal plain sediments of the time, Mesozoic in age. Afterward the area was again uplifted, and streams flowed southeastward on these sediments. Developing courses straight down the slope to the sea, they would, after cutting through the thin sedimentary cover, find their paths established transverse to the underlying structure. Such a history has been postulated to explain the fact that a number of major streams, such as the Delaware and the Susquehanna, now cut across the resistant ridges of the Appalachians. All the hypothetical cover has now been removed. Wherever a river crosses a ridge a water gap is formed, such as that of the Delaware River where it cuts through Kittatinny Mountain in eastern Pennsylvania.

The present ridges and valleys of the Folded Appalachians are, of course, the result of the differential erosion of this folded sequence of rocks, and the rather remarkable, even ridge tops are a reminder of the much earlier erosion surface, now uplifted. It should be emphasized that the present hills and ridges have come into being only by the hollowing out of the valleys between them. They were not pushed up as we see them now.

It is unrealistic to put back onto any present-day mountains the parts of the folds which have been removed and to assume that at any one time the mountain range resembled this resurrected folded surface, because weathering and erosion must begin to remove the upper parts of folds just as soon as they start to be formed. Fold mountains were never as high as a reconstruction of the eroded rocks would make them.

The drainage in the Folded Appalachians shows a trellis pattern. Most of the streams flow parallel to the ridges, and have very short tributaries at right angles. A few major rivers cut across the ridges. Such a trellis pattern is inevitable with folded structure because, as streams cut downward, those flowing on less resistant material will erode more rapidly and eventually outstrip those which initially flowed on the more resistant rocks. This type of drainage as well as the angular system in the Adirondacks, determined by intersecting joints and faults, and the roughly parallel arrangement of valleys on the coast of Maine, are all obviously due to weakness patterns in the bedrock of an area and are easily distinguished from the dendritic arrangement of streams which develops when there is no erosional control over the location of valleys. In order to understand such patterns it must be constantly borne in mind that rivers, in their youthful stage, are forever cutting downward and that they will cut most rapidly where the rocks are weakest. Thus, wherever there is any systematic difference in rock resistance, which reflects the structure of the rocks, the stream pattern will show it. A few drainage patterns, such as the parallel arrangement already mentioned along the Atlantic Coastal Plain and the radial pattern of streams flowing away from the top of a volcanic cone, are obviously due to the initial slope of a relatively new land surface and not to differences in rock resistance.

Extensive coal deposits are associated with the later sediments deposited in the Appalachian geosyncline. They originated in the Pennsylvanian period when layers of organic debris were deposited

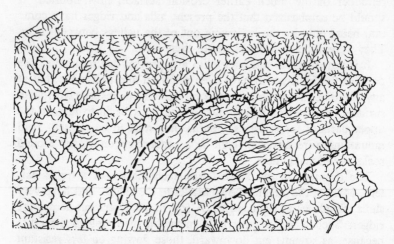

Drainage map of Pennsylvania. The outlined area has a trellis pattern characteristic of eroded folded rocks. Elsewhere, the pattern is dendritic.

between other sedimentary materials. The extensive forests whose remains are now coal grew on low-lying river floodplains and swampy regions near the inland geosynclinal sea. The subsidence of the area was spasmodic, which explains the presence of coal interbedded with marine deposits. By the Pennsylvanian period land plants were widespread. Fossil evidence for their first appearance is found in rocks of Silurian age.

The material which is now coal would have resembled peat at first in many respects, a water-logged, rather loosely packed mass of tree and plant debris. In the metamorphic series peat, lignite, bituminous coal, anthracite, and graphite, water and gaseous material decrease with each stage and the amount of carbon in proportion increases. The hard coal, anthracite, is found in the Folded Appalachians whereas the soft coal, bituminous, is found in the Plateau area, where diastrophism has been less intense and where the heat and pressure associated with folding has not changed the soft coal into hard coal. Since the coal is interbedded with the sedimentary layers it also has been faulted and folded along with them. In mining, it is necessary to follow an individual hard-coal seam often on a very steep slant, down into the earth to the bottom of a syncline and then upward toward the surface. Anthracite is now found hundreds of feet below sea level at the bottom of some of the synclines and in other places hundreds of feet above and heading for higher points now removed by weathering and erosion. In the bituminous areas, since the deformation has been less intense and the coal layers are more nearly horizontal, it is possible to strip the overlying sediments away in many cases and expose the coal so it can be more expeditiously excavated by power shovel.

The geologic history of the Rocky Mountains is similar to that of the Appalachians. Again, a geosyncline existed, in this case through the Mesozoic Era, at the end of which folding and faulting of the sediments occurred. This was followed by at least two stages of erosion. Apparently a peneplain was developed across the initially uplifted mountains and this was followed by a more recent uplift and the inauguration of the present cycle of mountain-carving. The present Rockies have thus been sculptured from rocks whose structure was created at the end of the Mesozoic. They have been uplifted more recently and to a higher elevation than the Appalachians, and thus they are more rugged at the present time. Glaciation in the higher parts of the Rockies has given the typical, jagged type of topography, missing in the lower Appalachians.

The folding of the Rockies was on a much broader scale than that of the Appalachians. Just west of Denver the mountains rise abruptly after a narrow zone of hogbacks, marking the upturned edges of resistant layers which at one time arched up over the higher parts of the mountains and continued miles westward to come down again in North Park. In the core of the Rockies a Precambrian granite has been exposed following the removal of the uplifted major fold.

Fault block mountains are formed by relatively large-scale vertical movements along steeply dipping normal faults. The Sierra Nevadas of California, the Grand Tetons of Wyoming, and many of the ranges in the Basin and Range Province of Utah and Nevada are excellent examples of such faulted blocks of the crust.

The Sierra Nevada Mountains, the largest single range in the United States, is a block of rock roughly 400 miles long, north to south, and 60 miles wide. It is bounded on the east by a very steep normal fault, dipping eastward, and by the Central Valley of California on the west. The crest line is not at the center of the range but lies within a very few miles of the eastern border. The higher parts have been well dissected by many valley glaciers which have left aretes, horns, and U-shaped valleys. Today there are a few small insignificant glaciers still left, lying in high cirques facing north and east.

The eastward slope from the crest of the Sierra Nevadas averages between 25 and 30 degrees. It is an erosion slope which has cut back and destroyed the initial fault declivity, which dipped much more steeply, perhaps 60 to 70 degrees. The slope of the major block to the west is approximately 3 degrees, but on this side rivers and glaciers have cut many valleys whose walls are much steeper than this.

Lake Tahoe, near the crest of the Range, lies in a basin bounded by subsidiary faults, roughly parallel to the major boundary fault on the east. The total amount of slippage along the latter fracture is measured in thousands of feet and took some millions of years to accomplish. The maximum shift was probably no more than a few tens of feet at a time.

Erosion, of course, started to destroy the Sierra Nevadas from the early stages of its formation, and the mountain was never as high as it would have been if the total faulting occurred at one time. The extensive removal of material has uncovered a granite core, which is very well exposed at Yosemite Valley.

In the Basin and Range Province many of the fault block mountains have been so deeply eroded that now only remnants are left, protruding through a thick cover of debris which has been washed down from the summits and piled around the lower parts. This is an area of interior drainage, where weathered material is not washed into the sea by throughgoing streams but is trapped in the low parts of the land. Here the scenic emphasis is on the very wide alluvium-filled valleys which lie between relatively narrow north-south-trending mountains, which must be traversed one after the other in crossing the area either from the east or from the west. The ranges have a very complex internal structure reflecting a long history of folding, faulting, and intrusion prior to block faulting. In places warm springs emerge in the valleys along lines which are parallel to the range fronts and a few miles distant. The water of such springs undoubtedly comes up along the fault zone connected with the formation of the blocks. They indicate that crustal instability here is of relatively recent occurrence, Upper Cenozoic, and perhaps also associated with the presence of magma at not too great a depth.

Mountain-building involves an upward movement of certain parts of the crust. Whether or not the vertical movement, even in the case of fold mountains, is the indirect result of horizontal compression is sometimes debatable. It seems inevitable, however, that in most cases, anyway where there is crustal compression of the surface layers, there must be some vertical uplift.

A successful theory of mountain-building must explain a variety of events, such as the compression needed to give folded and thrust faulted mountains, the downwarping of the geosynclinal stage, the belated uplift following the major orogeny, the vertical movements which are needed to produce fault block mountains, and the rather extensive strike-slip movements in parts of the crust.

In the nineteenth century it was believed by many that mountain-building was the result of the contraction of a once fluid earth under a solid crust. With contraction, they argued, the crust must wrinkle, because the area it once covered became less. It was thought that the cooling took about 100 million years and the circumference was lessened by tens if not hundreds of miles. However, since the discovery of radioactivity, and its heating effects, the idea of an original gaseous earth cooling steadily through a liquid to a solid condition was abandoned, but not necessarily the rest of the theory, which was simply based on a shortening of the crust in certain areas.

There is no doubt that strata in folded and faulted areas have been shortened and that opposite sides of a sedimentary pocket are now closer together than they were initially. The extent to which the entire crustal thickness partakes of the shortening is debatable. Most geologists at the present time feel that the folding and thrusting of rocks are probably confined to the upper portions of the crust and almost certainly do not go down into the mantle. In one view the entire crust may have been shortened to the same extent as the sedimentary strata in the major deformed belts, or perhaps the surface layers only need have been crumpled. Salt-dome dynamics illustrate on a small scale at least that the purely vertical intrusions of salt can be converted into horizontal displacements. The rocks at the top and sides of such structures have been tilted, domed, and broken with small faults.

The fact of crustal instability has, of course, been recognized for generations. However, there has historically been a difference of opinion with respect to exactly how widespread this instability was. For a long time the so-called eustatic theory prevailed. This assumes that continental areas of the world outside the relatively narrow mobile belts, where instability is active, have been stable throughout much of geologic time; that the coming and going of the ocean, first onto the land and then retreating, was due to the worldwide shifting of sea level, which in turn was brought about by changes in capacity of the ocean basins to hold water. The idea of the general stability of the land areas was strengthened by the recognized changes in sea level associated with the coming and going of times of glaciation. Such a general theory of the earth continued strong until the early years of the twentieth century when it was replaced by a recognition that there was more local crustal instability associated with continental upwarping and downsinkings than had been realized before, and that even parts of continents well away from the recognized organic or mobile belts have been unstable throughout geologic time.

Generally in mountain areas the observer notices only the erosional effects of the various gradational agents—valleys, waterfalls, cliffs, and peaks. His view is circumscribed. The major diastrophically produced landform must be appreciated in the mind, or on a map, or best of all from a vantage point high up in the air. Even here the visible picture is incomplete. Part of the vertical dimension is lacking. The extension of the structure, whether it be fold mountain, fault mountain, or volcano, must be imagined continuing underground, and the missing parts which have been eroded added to the heights. Furthermore, there is a fourth, time dimension. What we see now is but the passing aspect of a continually changing landscape. A projection of what the lands will look like, into at least the near geologic future, can be made by appreciating the inevitability of weathering and erosion. The changing scenes of the past can be resurrected by noting and evaluating evidences of past events preserved in the piles of sediments, intrusions, folds, faults, and erosion surfaces. We know that the modern scene has been produced by the action of forces and processes which we see working around us every day. The surface of the earth is in general a tattered surface. It is sculptured and the explanation for the various-shaped hills, valleys, cliffs, slopes, and hilltops is contained in a recognition that the agents of erosion are all attempting to wear the land down, and in this process they remove the weak and leave the strong.

The mere fact that after 4½ billion years there are still large mountain areas emphasizes the very important part played in the building up of land areas not only by volcanic activity, but by the folding, faulting, and arching of crustal layers. Why does diastrophism occur at all, and why does its location shift from place to place? These are major fundamental questions, which are to a large extent still not adequately answered.

(United Press International)

CHAPTER XV

ISOSTASY AND
EARTHQUAKES

The earth is essentially a sphere, approximately 8,000 miles in diameter. As the result of rotation there is a slight flattening at the poles and a bulging at the equator. The mathematical figure which most closely resembles this shape is an oblate spheroid, with an equatorial diameter of 7,927 miles and a polar diameter of 7,900 miles. The actual shape of the earth, the geoid, as given by sea level is still less regular because of the uneven distribution of land and water. Land areas draw the water up from the spheroid surface to a slight extent, thus the geoid lies above the spheroid in the continents and below it in the oceans. The detailed configuration of the solid earth is yet far more uneven, with mountain masses rising above the geoid in a very irregular fashion and the sea floor descending below it to give also a very rough topography. As measured against sea level, the maximum relief of the earth, that is, the difference between the highest and lowest points, is approximately 12 miles. Mount Everest reaches an elevation of 29,028 feet, about 5½ miles, and some of the deepest ocean trenches extend below sea level somewhat over six miles.

The earth as a whole shows two persistent levels, that of the continents which cover about 29 per cent of the globe, and that of the oceans. Approximately 25 per cent of the earth's surface, ⁶⁄₇ of land area, lies between sea level and 2,000 feet above; and 55 per cent of the earth's surface, almost ¾ of oceanic areas, lies between 10,000 and 20,000 feet below sea level. The mean elevation of the land is approximately 2,700 feet and the mean depth of the sea 12,400 feet. A comparison of the average elevations of the continents shows North America to have an elevation of 2,630 feet,

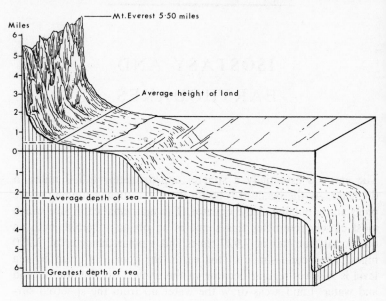

Schematic diagram showing the percentage of the earth's surface at various levels

Europe 1,150 feet, and Asia 3,200 feet.

Why is it that certain parts of the crust protrude as continental masses, while other parts are at a generally low elevation, well below sea level? A partial answer to this question can be given after a consideration of variations in the force of gravity from one place to another. The force of gravity is dependent primarily on the total mass of the earth and the distance from the center; the greater the mass and the closer one is to the center, the greater will be the attraction. At the equator an observer is slightly further away from the center, and the force of gravity there will be less than at the poles. Gravity will also be somewhat less due to the rotation of the earth and the development of centrifugal force. As a result of these two factors, the sea-level force of gravity in terms of the acceleration given a freely fallen body is 978.049 cm/sec/sec* at the equator and 985.221 cm/sec/sec at the poles. Gravity also varies from place to place on the earth's surface, depending on the density of the material directly underlying the station where the measurements are made. Deviations from the normal are gravity anomalies.

Measurements have shown that under the major mountain ranges there is less mass than under neighboring lower areas. Such lack of mass is one of deficiency near the surface where the rocks are less dense than normal. The same situation, but on a much larger scale, is true of continental areas as contrasted with oceanic. It would appear that the continents and the mountains are high because they are buoyed up by low-density roots, that they act just like any floating object and follow Archimedes' principle for such bodies. Blocks of the earth's crust tend to rise or sink so that, given time for adjustment to occur, their masses are hydrostatically supported from below, except where local stresses are currently acting to upset equilibrium. Such in essence is the Law of Isostasy. The crust acts like a scale; if material is added from one part to another the loaded area will sink and the area from which material has been removed will rise. Any change in the load on the earth's surface is accompanied by a postulated slow lateral flowage of plastic rock at depth.

There are two possible physical explanations for the observed density distribution. In one, the density of the crust varies from place to place, the less dense rocks sticking up farther. Another suggestion is that the density of the columns of crustal material is the same from place to place, but that the depth to which they extend varies. This theory resembles what happens in the case of an iceberg, where the bergs which stick up farthest above the ocean have correspondingly the deepest extensions under water. Obviously in these explanations, both probably true in varying cases, the assumption is made that materials at depth are more

* Centimeters per second per second

dense than the crustal rocks which "float" on them. The term "float" here should be used advisedly. We know that the earth except for the core acts like a solid under short-term stresses. Apparently under longer continuing stresses it will adjust by a slow flowage.

The Law of Isostasy explains how mountain masses undergoing erosion will continue to rise for quite some time, thus supplying fresh material to be weathered and eroded, and why areas of sedimentation will sink under the added load. The fact that the earth does react in this way, when large masses continental in size down to mountain ranges are considered, has been demonstrated most dramatically by the postglacial rebound from the ice cover in the northern parts of North America and Scandinavia. The maximum rise of the land in the Gulf of Bothnia, in Scandinavia, for instance, has been approximately 250 meters since 6800 B.C. The existence of isostasy implies two things: the crust is too weak to support a large mass and the denser earth materials under the surface layers must "flow" so as to adjust themselves to changes in the load which they carry.

A comparison of the major relief features of continents and ocean basins shows that the results of diastrophism are apparently similar in each. Profiles across such areas resemble each other, showing in general a very irregular surface. Mountain chains, arcuate ridges, chains of volcanoes, deep trenches, and flat areas are found in the oceans, and generally the same configurations prevail on the land, where the deeper downwarped geosynclinal parts, however, have been filled with sediments, as we have seen.

The Pacific Ocean Basin, where approximate isostatic equilibrium exists between the various parts, has, like all oceans, a thin dense crust compared with the continents. The local relief is largely of volcanic origin. Here, the geologic boundaries may be drawn in various ways, with the type of lava associated with the volcanism commonly used as a basis. Ocean depths of less than four kilometers are generally associated with the continental, andesite-producing areas, and over four kilometers with the major basalt-producing part of the Pacific Basin. Island arcs and their associated trenches lie on the continental side of the Andesite Line.

The materials dredged up from any of the oceanic areas are relatively young. Sediments range in age from Recent to Cretaceous and the most ancient basalt from the sea floor is merely 50 million years old, that is, early Tertiary. Have earlier oceanic crusts been swept up and incorporated into continents by some mechanism, have they been overlain by more recent materials, or what other history explains the observations? As we shall see, there is no clearcut answer. There is very good evidence that bodies of seawater have existed for over 3 billion years and have supported life for ⅔ of this length of time.

The crust of the earth is on the average about 20 miles thick under the continents and five miles in oceanic areas. It is this part of the earth which, as we have seen, differs markedly in density from place to place, and as long as this difference has prevailed there must have been continents and ocean basins.

The fundamental causes for the formation of the ocean basins and continents, the origin of major mountain ranges, the problem of fixed versus drifting continents, and the very early geologic history of the earth are some of the major problems which are interesting geologists at the present time. In order to attempt an answer to these and other problems involving the major dynamics of the earth, it is necessary to learn as much as possible about the composition and the condition of the materials at all levels from the surface to the center. Various ways have been devised to investigate the deeper parts, the most direct method being to dig holes and bring up samples from as far down as possible. Some of the deepest holes dug in the earth are those drilled to find oil, and mines have been excavated to extract useful materials. A very few miles at most of the crust have been sampled in this direct fashion, however.

Long and active erosion has uncovered in a number of places material which was at one time at even greater depth. The presence of any kind of metamorphic rock necessitates extensive erosion, and the types of minerals present in the metamorphic rock give some ideas as to the depth of formation with its associated temperatures and pressures. Low-pressure minerals are those in which in general the atoms are arranged in an open, loose network, and the higher the pressure the more closely packed together they are. Kyanite, Al_2SiO_5, is a mineral formed only under the high temperatures and pressures prevailing at depth and associated with high-grade metamorphism. Its presence at the surface indicates uplift with resulting erosion of 10 to 12 miles or more.

Magma originates a number of miles down, in the upper part of the mantle in places, and lava samples can be collected for analysis. Such samples of course will give at best only the bulk chemical composition of the magma, which furthermore may have been modified by contact with higher-level rocks.

Information concerning the density of materials at depth can be obtained by weighing the earth. This is done very simply by recourse to the Law of Gravitation. The total mass of the earth is calculated, and then, knowing the volume, its mean density. The mean density of the earth as a whole is 5.517 gr/cm^3 and of the surface rocks is 2.8 gr/cm^3. Thus there must be much denser material at depth, so that the average can be more than the surface rocks.

The actual way in which the density varies within the earth is difficult to determine. It is reasonable, however, that the heaviest materials should be at the core and materials of less density toward the surface. Outside the rocky crust of the earth there is the still lighter incomplete water layer, the hydrosphere, and on top of that the least dense layer, the atmosphere, which in turn varies to the most attenuated state farthest out.

A core composed or iron and nickel and a less dense silicate composition for the overlying mantle gives a reasonable density distribution for the earth. Furthermore, if it is assumed that meteorites are representative samples of the same type of solar system material as that composing the earth, they in their two forms, metallic and stony, bear out this picture.

Most information about the earth's interior has been obtained from the study of earthquake waves. An analysis of such seismic waves shows velocity variations, and by comparing laboratory experiments on rocks of various kinds it is possible to come to a conclusion as to the type and arrangement of rock which occurs at depth. The requisite pressure and temperature of course must be given the test specimens in order to have a proper comparison.

To summarize, less than 0.03 per cent of the earth's radius, about 12 miles at most, is directly visible in mines, drill cores, and deeply eroded parts of the crust, and the composition and state of the rest of the earth must be indirectly determined by a study of earthquake waves, by a reasoning from density measurements and from a comparison with meterorites.

Earthquakes occur in well-defined areas, in general very closely associated with volcanic activity and the most rugged and highest mountains. These are all manifestations, of course, of crustal instability. Eighty per cent of the large earthquakes and over 80 per cent of the smaller ones occur in close proximity to the well-known circum-Pacific volcanic area.

Many measurable earthquakes occur every year. Probably over 150,000 occur annually which are large enough to be felt by people nearby, and instruments record an earth total many times this number.

There have been many historic earthquakes, remembered because of large loss of life and destruction. For instance, the great Lisbon earthquake of the first of November, 1755, caused the death of approximately 60,000 people out of a population of 235,-000. One house in six was habitable after the quake. Much of the destruction was the result of seismic sea waves. The sea withdrew from the harbor and returned as a wall of water 50 feet high, causing a fantastic amount of damage.

The low-frequency surface waves of some of the major earthquakes, if they correspond with the natural frequency of oscillation of an enclosed body of water, may set it into oscillatory wave motion or seiches, by a resonance mechanism. At Yarmouth Harbor on the coast of England, 1,090 miles from the center of the Lisbon quake, six-foot waves were built up, Loch Lomond in Scotland reported two-foot waves, and waves in Scandinavian lakes 1,820 miles away were reported to have been formed. The period of natural vibrations varied from a few seconds in small ponds to ten minutes in Loch Lomond. Destruction to buildings is also much greater if the natural vibration time of the building corresponds to ground vibration. The building can be made to vibrate with much greater amplitude than that of the ground surface. There is an exact anology between this effect and getting a heavy weight to swing in wider and wider arcs with the periodic application of a small force at the appropriate time.

New Madrid, Missouri, was the center of an earthquake which occurred on the 16th of December, 1811. At 2 A.M., the earth cracked open, mud and water gushed out burying fields, the banks of the Mississippi caved in, and large tracts of the floodplain either rose or fell. Reelfoot Lake, Tennessee, 18 miles long and three miles wide was formed at this time by a depression of the river floodplain, between the river itself and the bluffs at the side. Changes in the course of the Mississippi River occurred and a total of 3,000 to 5,000 square miles was scarred with the effects of this quake. Pressures built up in underlying sand layers resulted in so-called sand blows where water and sand escaped to the surface under high pressure. Altogether, there were three major quakes and many minor shocks felt between December 16, 1811, and February 7, 1812. The quakes were felt from the Rocky Mountains to the Atlantic Ocean and from Canada to the Gulf of Mexico.

On the 10th of September, 1899, the southeastern coast of Alaska was shaken by an earthquake, originating in the Yakutat Bay area. A large vertical displacement was noted following the quake. Barnacles and boring clams on the sea floor were raised 47 feet above sea level in one place, and elsewhere areas were depressed.

The San Francisco earthquake of April 18, 1906, was classic. The intensity of earth motion was greater outside the city; however, the destruction to man-made structures, from both the quake and the resulting fire, was most costly in the built-up areas of San Francisco. This earthquake resulted from motion along the San Andreas Fault where slippage occurred over a length of more than 200 miles, from Point Arena on the north to San Juan on the south. The maximum horizontal motion as shown by displaced roads, fence posts, and similar features was approximately 21 feet, on the shore near Tomales Bay.

The San Francisco earthquake was significant in the development of seismology because the elastic rebound theory was proposed in explanation of it, and the very extensive damage led to the adoption of better building standards.

Two of the most recent destructive quakes occurred in Chile in

May, 1960, and in Alaska on the 27th of March, 1964. Note that these earthquakes as well as the San Francisco and Yakutat Bay ones lie in the circum-Pacific zone of activity. The focus of the Chilean quake was on a north-south fault plane at a depth of approximately 31 miles. Various subsidiary shocks were located at different positions along the same fault, and the area of disaster was about 500 miles long. The results of this quake included a tsunami, or seismic sea wave, which was felt as far away as Hawaii and Japan, and was probably produced by an offshore subsidence of the sea floor along the fault trace. Actually, no evidence was found on land of fault movement reaching the surface; therefore the quake was undoubtedly the result of this offshore faulting. In places saturated mud flowed as a thick liquid under the influence of the vibration, hundreds of landslides occurred, some rivers were dammed up, and a lava flow emerged from a new vent on the side of a volcano.

The great Alaskan earthquake of the 27th of March, 1964, released probably twice as much energy as the 1906 San Francisco quake. The epicenter was in the northern part of Prince William Sound, between Anchorage and Valdez. In Anchorage landslides were the principal cause of destruction. There, parts of an outwash deposit laid on a relatively weak clay moved as more or less coherent masses. An uninhabited island off the coast was lifted more than 30 feet and a stretch of the sea floor 1,300 feet wide was left exposed. Again, no faulting was evident on the land but twisting of the crust was shown. A large area of uplift embracing a segment of the continental shelf paralleled an area of subsidence to the northwest. The depth of the initial break was between 20 and 50 kilometers and many after-shocks were located on a plane 800 kilometers long which dipped northwest toward the land.

At Valdez, the waterfront facilities were destroyed by a wave which was generated by a submarine landslide on the steep front of the deltas on which the town is built. Elsewhere bridges were twisted and rocked off their foundations, highways tossed about, and concrete shells of buildings fractured in geometric patterns.

This earthquake established again that the softer and wetter the ground the greater the amplitude of the earthquake waves, and therefore the greater the damage. Actually the quake occurred before the frost was out of the ground and thus damage was probably much less than it would otherwise have been. The quake produced tsunamis which were 30 to 35 feet high at Kodiak, 12 feet high at Crescent City in northern California, and 3 to 4 feet high in the Argentine Islands on the western side of the Palmer Peninsula in Antarctica, the waves reaching these islands 22 hours after the quake. In addition to sea waves, waves in the air were generated by the rapid change in ground level. These were detected and recorded on microbarographs at both Berkeley and La Jolla in California.

Tsunamis, associated with the major quakes in the Pacific region, have been known for years and a Pacific warning system was set up in Honolulu in 1948 by the United States Coast and Geodetic Survey to warn countries around the Pacific Basin of their coming. Twenty-five tsunamis were recorded in the Pacific Basin between 1956 and 1964. Such sea waves cannot be noted in the open ocean, any more than the rising and falling of the tides. In deep water they travel at the fantastic speed of 600 m.p.h., but are slowed up very markedly in shallow water. Their origin is commonly associated with faulting along the sea floor where a section of the ocean bottom drops with respect to another part and thus sets these large waves in motion. Some result from violent submarine volcanic eruptions, and others are due to submarine landslides.

The death toll from tsunamis has been very large, especially along the populated coastal plains of many of the countries bordering the western Pacific. Over 36,000 were killed in 1883 in the East Indies (Indonesia) by such a wave, and in 1896, 27,000 lost their lives in Japan. In 1946 damage of $25,000,000 was done on the Hawaiian Islands and 150 were killed.

The major source of earthquake waves, that is, the faulting, consists of two parts, the mass movement of a whole strained region at the time of release, and the grating along the surface of the fault plane, one block of the crust on another. Such grating is considered the major cause of the waves which emanate from the break. With very few exceptions, quakes which accompany the movement of lava underground are relatively small. As we will see the very deepest earthquakes are probably due to some other mechanism than faulting, perhaps the collapse of the crust into a hole, produced by a phase change in the rocks.

The elastic rebound theory for the origin of earthquake waves was developed by H. F. Reid following the 1906 San Francisco earthquake, and it provides a satisfactory model for at least the shallow and intermediate earthquakes. This theory assumes the slow buildup of elastic strain and its eventual release in a very short length of time by slippage along a fault. The fact that elastic strain does develop has been demonstrated in the San Andreas Fault area in California. The two opposed sides of this part of the crust twist at the relatively high rate of about five centimeters per year, the western side northward. The strains are essentially confined to a zone six miles wide on either side of the fault, and an earthquake is felt each time they are relieved by faulting. The total accumulated adjustment here has been some hundreds of miles in the last few millions of years.

Vibrations set up by faulting in a solid such as the earth are of various types. Motion may be up and down, sideways or forward and backward, or there may be a combination of these. The seismograph, a machine for detecting and measuring ground motion, amplifies and makes a record of the vibrations. The seismogram, or record, consists of a succession of vibrations divided into groups of varying appearance. The first group of ground vibrations to arrive at a receiving station are the so-called primary or "P" waves which represent motion of the ground either toward or away from the focus of faulting. They resemble sound waves in that they are longitudinal, with a zone of slight compression in the rocks followed by one of less compression. The second group of waves, the secondary or "S" waves, appear after the P waves. They travel through the rocks at a slower rate, and are transverse in motion, that is, the ground vibrates sideways to the direction in which the wave is traveling.

The origin of earthquake waves such as the longitudinal type can be imagined in connection with an underground explosion which takes place in a small hollow. Initially the walls of rock move outward until the elastic back pressure of the compressed rock equals the outward pressure of the gaseous products of the explosion, and slightly more, since the outward velocity of the moving rock must be slowed to zero. After this, the walls move back, but the zone of compression initially given to the rock surrounding the explosion compresses the rock still farther away, and thus a compression wave is propagated outward in all directions. This is followed by an outward-moving zone of slightly less compressed material; in this way a number of waves will emanate from the initial shock before motion dies down. The energy of the rock motion eventually is converted into heat produced by the friction of rock particles as they move in response to the compression and decompression cycles.

Transverse wave motion is inaugurated by a shearing type of action, where a mass of rock in attempting to slide over another mass gives it a sideways motion. Such motion is then transferred from one block to another until it too dies out, the energy dissipated into heat.

In addition to the primary and secondary waves, the so-called body waves which are propagated through the earth, faulting sets the surface of the land into an up-and-down motion with slight forward and backward components. Such undulations resembling water waves, are the large or "L" waves and are the last to arrive at a receiving station from an earthquake center.

In contrast to the P type of wave which can pass through solids, liquids, or gases, the S waves can only be propagated through a solid. They depend upon the ability of one part of a material to transmit a sideways motion to a neighboring part, and not a push and pull motion characteristic of the P waves. A sideways shear obviously cannot be transmitted by a liquid or a gas.

The earth can be set into motion by other less violent mechanisms than faulting, volcanic activity, or sudden volume changes. Nowhere is the ground completely at rest; so-called microseisms occur at all places on the earth's surface, with great differences in intensity, however, from place to place. Such small shakings of the earth are due to a variety of causes, such as wind on trees, slopes and buildings, strong pressure gradients in the atmosphere, surf beating on the shore, and especially in cities, traffic. Seismograph stations are located where such microseisms are at a minimum so that the record of distant earthquakes may be as clear as possible.

The first effective seismograph was built in 1880, and the first identified seismic wave from a distance was recorded in a seismogram made on the 17th of April, 1889, when a seismograph in Potsdam, Germany, registered an earthquake which originated in Japan. The standard seismograph depends on the principle of inertia. A heavy mass is suspended and the ground shifts underneath it, and this relative motion is recorded in some fashion. For a complete record of earth movements, seismographs must be designed to measure motion in the vertical and two horizontal directions, generally north-south and east-west. Furthermore, to obtain the most complete record, a battery of instruments must be used which are sensitive to and can detect vibrations of all possible earth frequencies from a fraction of a second to several minutes.

There are four major measurable quantities associated with earthquakes: the location of the epicenter, that is, the place on the surface of the earth directly over the focus or point of initial breakage; the depth to the focus; the exact time at which breaking starts; and the magnitude of the quake. Furthermore, the following can at times be determined: the length of the surface trace of the fault connected with the earthquake, the orientation of the fault plane, the duration of faulting, and the velocity with which rupture moves from the point of initial break to the point where it dies out.

A specific origin in time and location can be given to an earthquake even though it is believed that in large earthquakes the actual process of fracturing goes on for some minutes and spreads from an initial point of first breakage. This can be done, since apparently the fracturing extends itself less rapidly than earthquake waves move outward through unfractured rocks. The first break sends out the initial P and S waves, which are picked up and by which the timing and location of the quake are made.

The distance to an epicenter from a seismograph station can be determined from the seismogram. The average speeds of the P and S waves through the crust are known, 7.0 kilometers per second and 3.8 kilometers per second, respectively, and therefore by measuring the time lag of arrival of the S wave after the P wave it is possible to calculate the distance. They obviously both started together, and the farther they travel the more the S wave will lag behind the P wave. An exact location of occurrence by observations from one station only cannot be made. All that can be done is to draw around such a station a circle whose radius is at the proper epicentral distance. Information from three or more seismograph stations, however, will give an exact locality, since circles drawn around three stations must uniquely intersect in only one point. Furthermore, once the distance is found, the exact time of rupture can also be figured. The time of arrival is noted, the distance is figured, and, knowing the speed of either type of wave, it is a simple matter to calculate the time when they started.

Earthquakes are commonly classified by the depth at which motion is initiated. Shallow earthquakes occur down to a depth of 70 kilometers, intermediate 70 to 300 kilometers, and deep earthquakes from 300 down to as much as 720 kilometers below the earth's surface. It has been estimated that probably over 75 per cent of all earthquakes have a relatively shallow origin, and have resulted from fracturing in the crust.

The number of earthquakes drops off with increasing depth of focus, to about 250 kilometers, after which the number at various increasing depths to 700 kilometers is irregular. Very deep earthquakes have unusually weak surface waves associated with them and are felt over a very wide area, with intensities uniform for large distances. In shallow earthquakes the severity of ground motion drops off very rapidly away from the epicenter, being about 10 per cent at a distance of 25 miles.

The intensity of an earthquake in a specific place is commonly given in terms of the damage done. On the Rossi-Forel scale the maximum extent of damage is at 10 and the minimum at 1. In the newer Mercalli scale the intensity 12 is given to the region of maximum damage. Intensity 1 is not felt by anyone except under very favorable conditions, when slight dizziness may be experienced, and intensity 12 is associated with general panic and total damage to buildings. The intervening numbered divisions distribute damage between these two extremes.

The intensity of an earthquake varies greatly from place to place and depends not only on the actual amount of energy released at the focus and the distance therefrom but also on the nature of the material between the source and the observer. Isoseismal lines drawn on a map to join points with equal intensities are never circular. Because the source of seismic energy instead of being at a point is generally a plane, the release of energy is not necessarily uniform in all directions. In addition different types of rock vary in efficiency in transmitting vibrations.

In an attempt to compare the source energies between one earthquake and another C. F. Richter in 1935 designed a magnitude scale, based on the measure of the amplitude of motion shown on a specific type of seismograph 100 kilometers from the epicenter of a quake. There is no fixed maximum in this scale, but the largest known earthquake in the first half of the twentieth century was 8.6. The magnitude 7.0 and over is considered a major earthquake, and 2.5 is just large enough to be felt nearby. The Alaskan earthquake of March, 1964, had a magnitude of 8.5. The Richter scale is logarithmic and an increase of one whole number means an amplitude increase, as measured on the instrument, of ten, and an energy release a number of times greater.

If the earth were perfectly elastic, seismic waves once formed would continue indefinitely; thus each quake would add to the vibrations of earth materials. Fortunately, however, this is not the case and seismic energy is transformed eventually into heat energy.

The actual intensity of any series of seismic waves is limited by the breaking strength of rocks. The elastic rebound theory calls on a buildup of strain until the rocks must give, and then fracturing occurs. Since rocks have a finite strength at which they will break, the amount of energy associated with faulting and resulting earthquake waves is limited. However, an earthquake can be very destructive since stresses can be built up over the total length of the fault plane.

The displacement of the surface rocks connected with an earthquake, that is, the actual relative slippage, has been observed to be from a few centimeters in a small shock to 47 feet in the fault of September, 1899, in Yakutat Bay in Alaska. The horizontal extent of breakage, that is, the length of the fault plane, also varies with the size of the quake, from a few tens of feet up to hundreds of miles. One of the longest directly observed breaks associated with an earthquake was that along the San Andreas Fault in the quake of 1906, which extended for 250 miles. The actual length was somewhat more, extending an unknown distance out to sea.

The duration of slippage at any one point is not accurately known but has been estimated to be from a fraction of a second to ten seconds or so in some of the largest quakes.

The speed of propagation of rupture from an initial point of breakage, probably varies between three and four kilometers a second. These values have been determined from an analysis of some of the surface waves. If one assumes four kilometers per second for the speed of propagation of rupture and that in a 1,000-kilometer-long fault the break starts at the middle and spreads to each end, the duration of rupturing would be 500 divided by 4, or 125 seconds.

Most of the great deep earthquakes of the world occur along the rim of the Pacific, as we have noted, where there is a close connection with volcanoes and deep trenches. Here the various faults with which the quakes are associated parallel the continental margins. They dip landward and intersect the surface of the earth somewhat offshore in the majority of cases, and thus their length cannot be directly measured. A probable length of at least a thousand kilometers was given to the Chilean earthquake of May 20, 1960, by an analysis of surface waves and the distribution pattern of the after-shocks.

The very deepest earthquakes may be due to some other mechanism than faulting, because the frictional stress needed is greater than the shearing strength of known rocks. That is, rocks would shatter at great depths rather than shear, unless friction along the fault plane were decreased somehow by partial liquefaction resulting in easier slippage, or by a sort of reduced rolling friction of particles. It has been suggested that a possible mechanism for the origin of very deep earthquakes could be the collapse of a small volume of rock, caused by the sudden change of one type of mineralogy into another denser type. For a large quake the volume of rock need not be more than $\frac{1}{3}$ of a kilometer or so in diameter. Furthermore, an analysis of such deep quakes apparently shows that their source volumes are very small.

There have been very marked improvements in the analysis of earthquakes and in the actual detectors for them, in the last few years. Detectors now cover the whole range of the seismic spectrum and can record ground vibrations with periods from more than 1,000 seconds, the maximum that occurs in the earth, down to a very small fraction of a second. Seismic waves have been detected which have gone around the earth a number of times, and others have been noted which have been reflected from the earth's core. In some cases it has been possible to determine the actual orientation of the fault plane, that is, its strike and dip, from an analysis of seismic wave data coming to a station from different directions.

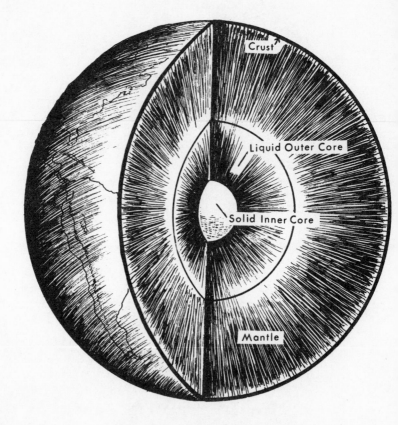

The major layers of the earth

CHAPTER XVI

EARTH STRUCTURE

The general structure of the earth, with its major layers, is relatively clear. The outermost atmosphere and hydrosphere overlie the crust, which varies in thickness from an average of 22 miles under the continents to six miles under the seas. The change in the velocity of earthquake waves as they leave the crust and enter the mantle is abrupt and marks the Mohorovicic Discontinuity, or more briefly, the "M" Discontinuity. It was discovered in 1909 when A. Mohorovicic, a seismologist in Yugoslavia was analyzing the seismogram of a Balkan earthquake. He found the record of two groups of waves, the slower one coming directly through the crust, and the faster taking the longer but more rapid path, deep into the earth and then back to the surface. The change in seismic wave velocity with depth seemed to be an abrupt one, occurring at about 30 miles down. Such a variation in velocity which was true for both the P and S waves indicates physical changes which probably reflect differences in either the bulk chemical composition or in pressure-induced alterations in the rock materials.

The mantle, under the crust, extends downward to a depth of 1,800 miles and the core has a radius of 2,200 miles. The actual volume of the core is about $\frac{1}{6}$ of the earth, and the mantle volume $\frac{5}{6}$. Each one can be divided, on the basis of seismic wave data, into a lower and an upper part with perhaps a transitional zone separating the two.

There is enough homogeneity in the crust and upper mantle so that by an analysis of the time lag between the P and S waves an epicenter for earthquakes can be determined. Nevertheless, in detail, the crustal rocks are measurably heterogeneous and the M Discontinuity divides these rocks, which as we have seen have nearly perfect isostatic equilibrium, from an apparently more homogeneous mantle.

A generalized section across the continental and oceanic parts of the crust shows the M Discontinuity at the base, separating the mantle from the sima, which has a worldwide distribution. Overlying the sima is the sial, which appears only in continental areas, the water of the oceans resting directly on the sima, with perhaps in places a thin layer of sediments separating the two. Furthermore, where the sial pinches out at the margins of the continents, and in various downwarped areas elsewhere, there are layers of sediments, resting on the sial. The total thickness of the crust in the continental areas where the less dense sial is present is thicker than in the oceanic areas. Isostatic equilibrium calls for a column of continental crust (sima and sial) to have the same weight as a column of oceanic crust, both extended down into the mantle to the same depth. Of course the cross-sectional areas of the two columns must be the same. Land areas are higher in continents but the M Discontinuity is also lower there.

The continental slope is the place where the continental crust grades into the oceanic. As the thick wedge of continental materials thins out and the land dips under the sea, the M Discontinuity approaches the surface. For instance, off the southern California coast at one place the sea floor within a distance of 20 kilometers drops from 1 to 3.5 kilometers below sea level, while the M level changes from 18 to 12 kilometers deep. Here the continental slope is about 7 degrees and the M level slope is approximately 18 degrees in the opposite direction.

The data upon which conclusions concerning the interior parts of the earth are based are approximate and preliminary in many cases. Furthermore, approximations have been made which are undoubtedly untrue in detail at least, for example, that which assumes that the layers of the earth are uniform throughout. We know that the crust in detail is not and there is evidence that seems to indicate that the upper mantle may not be as homo-geneous as was formerly believed.

The term "crust" for the surface layer of the earth comes from the early concept of an initially liquid earth which cooled and crusted over at the surface. It is now believed that the earth probably never did pass through a gaseous, then liquid to a solid state,

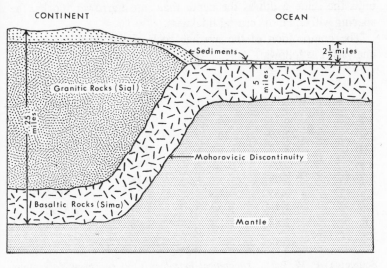

Generalized diagram of the earth's crust at a continental border

but was formed by the accretion of solid particles.

In the crust the P waves travel less than 7.2 kilometers per second and the S waves less than 3.8 kilometers per second. Both, in general, increase in velocity from the surface downwards. There is a jump in velocity of the P waves from 6.1 to 6.4 kilometers per second which apparently marks the change from the granitic to the basaltic layers in the continental crust. The mantle lying directly under the crust transmits the P waves in its upper parts with a velocity of 7.8-8.2 kilometers per second, and the S waves move at 4.5 kilometers per second. Both crust and mantle are solid except for small pockets of magma. They are known to be solid because both transmit the secondary or shear type of waves. The core of the earth, on the other hand, is believed to be liquid, at least in its outer part, because it will not transmit the secondary waves.

Verification for crustal thicknesses obtained by a study of earthquake waves has been suggested from the spacing of volcanoes. When cones occur in a row, they tend to be uniformly spaced. If we assume that volcanoes occur where cross-fractures cut a principal fracture, and that the crust can be broken more easily into units the same width as the depth than into narrower blocks, the spacing will equal the crustal thickness.

The composition of the average rock of the crust exposed to analysis is as follows:

Element	Weight %	Atom %	Volume %	Atomic Radii (Angstrom Units)
O	46.71	60.5	94.24	1.40
Si	27.69	20.5	0.51	0.39
Al	8.07	6.2	0.44	0.50
Fe	5.05	1.9	0.37	0.70
Mg	2.08	1.8	0.28	0.65
Ca	3.65	1.9	1.04	0.99
Na	2.75	2.5	1.21	0.95
K	2.58	1.4	1.88	1.33
	98.58			

Source: T. F. W. Barth, *Theoretical Petrology* (2nd ed.; New York: John Wiley, 1962), p. 17.

Note that eight out of the 92 naturally occurring elements comprise by weight over 98 per cent of the earth's crust, and that if the elements are compared by volume, over 94 per cent of the surface rock is composed of oxygen. We actually walk on a platform of oxygen as we travel across the land.

Seismic wave velocities do change at various depths in the earth, as we have seen, and these changes are not always regular but may be sudden at specific depths. There is a difference of opinion, however, as to just what such data mean in terms of the type or state of the rocks present. The M level may represent a change in the bulk chemical composition of material, or it may represent a different arrangement of the atoms. The average specific gravity of the crust is about 2.84, and it is believed that in the upper mantle it is well over 3. Thus, on the average, either an assemblage of heavier elements is present or the lighter elements of the crust are packed more closely together. If the upper mantle is composed of essentially the same material as the lower crust, that is basalt, it must exist in a denser form. Such a rock, eclogite, is known. If the upper mantle is composed of an assemblage of heavier elements, it may resemble the rock peridotite. Unfortunately, seismic wave data cannot distinguish between eclogite and peridotite, because both rocks transmit earthquake waves at approximately the same speed.

The basalt which emerges from many volcanoes originates in the upper mantle, so that there is no doubt that material of that composition does occur there. And a sample of basalt can be converted into a garnet-pyroxene assemblage of minerals typical of eclogites by heating it in the laboratory for approximately an hour at 1200 degrees C and under a pressure equal to 30 kilobars, or the pressure due to the overlying rocks at a depth of about 60 miles. Furthermore, eclogite has been found in metamorphic rocks from many continental areas, an obvious relic of high temperatures and pressures.

The composition of the mantle, like the crust, is probably mostly oxygen, with silicon, iron, and magnesium. Collectively, these four elements may equal more than 90 per cent of the total mass. The possible ways in which they may be put together can be investigated in the laboratory by experimenting with germanium and germinates, which are similar in chemistry and structure to silicon and silicates, but which undergo similar transformations at a lower temperature and pressure than do the silicates. Thus they can be used more easily to see what happens with silicates as we go deeper and deeper into the mantle. Under pressure both germanium and silicon are packed closer together with their neighboring oxygen atoms. At surface temperatures and pressures the silicates have a basic structure of four oxygen atoms surrounding one silicon atom. Under high pressures this number is increased to six, and the specific gravity increases in proportion. At the present time investigators can reach in the laboratory the temperatures and pressure ranges which exist in the upper mantle.

There are three major parts to the mantle, as indicated by earthquake wave data, the upper down to 400 kilometers, a transition zone 400 to 900 kilometers in depth and the lower mantle 900 to 2,900 kilometers down. In the transition zone the rapid increase in the velocity of seismic waves may reflect an increase in density which can be explained by a series of reactions in which the silicates are rearranged into more closely packed atomic structures. In addition to these major mantle divisions a discontinuity in wave velocities has been discovered at a depth of about 300 miles. It is called the 20-degree discontinuity because its influence is noted on seismograms 20 degrees from the epicenter of an earthquake.

The composition of iron meteorites suggests that the earth's core is probably composed of nickel and iron. The inner section is presumed to be solid in contrast to the outer liquid part. Earthquake waves travel at slightly different speeds in the two regions, and reflections of seismic waves have been obtained from the inner solid. The inner core may be composed of materials similar to those in the outer but are in a solid state because of the higher pressures prevailing there. Convection currents in the fluid part may give rise to the earth's magnetic field, the core in this case acting like a dynamo with moving charged particles.

The nickel-iron core has been confirmed to a certain degree by experiments with explosively generated shock pressures believed to equal those at the core. Special instruments have been devised to record the very fleeting changes in properties of samples under such transitory high pressures. The shock data permit a mixture of nickel and iron for the core, but not of lighter weight elements. Furthermore, the core apparently cannot be composed of pure iron, because under the pressure conditions there the density would be 10 to 15 per cent too great. A mixture with nickel, however, gives the proper density.

The existence of the core was proved by I. D. Oldham of England in 1906 from the analysis of seismic data, and in 1914 Beno Gutenberg showed that the core-mantle boundary was about ½ the way from the surface to the center of the earth. The depth to the outer core has now been determined to be 1,800 miles and the depth to the more recently discovered inner core 3,100 miles.

The density of the mantle increases slowly with depth from

somewhat over 3 to almost 6 gr/cm³.* At the core the density is believed to jump to between 9 and 10 gr/cm³, and to increase slowly to a value between 11 and 12 at the inner core boundary where it may take another jump, according to some geologists, to over 13 gr/cm³ in the inner core.

There are two ways in which the density of a given substance

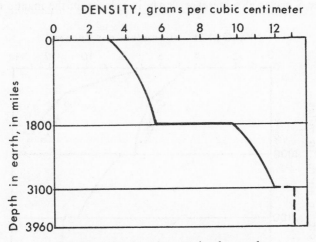

Probable density changes in the earth

will increase with added pressure. Simple compression reduces the distance between atoms, resulting in a gradual increase, or a sudden change may result from a rearrangement of the way in which the atoms are packed together. They always tend to arrange themselves in the configuration which is most stable for a given temperature and pressure. At the base of the mantle the pressure is 1,-400,000 times that of the atmosphere and at the center of the earth it is 3,400,000 times. (Atmospheric pressure=14.5 pounds per square inch.)

The velocities of seismic waves in the mantle increase toward the core, with apparently a low-velocity layer in the upper mantle. The P wave velocity changes from about 8 kilometers per second

* Grams per cubic centimeter

to nearly 14 kilometers per second. A sudden drop in velocity back
to 8 kilometers per second occurs at the mantle-core boundary. In
the outer core the velocity increases gradually to about 10 kilometers per second, and at the inner core boundary it takes a jump
to over 11 kilometers per second. The lower velocity layer in the
upper mantle, about 300 miles deep, marks a zone where the rocks
may be more plastic.

The S waves also increase slowly in velocity in the mantle from

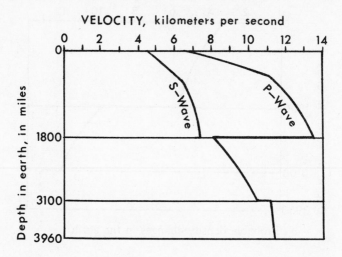

Seismic wave velocity changes in the earth, generalized

somewhat over four to seven kilometers per second at the core
boundary. These waves do not penetrate the core and thus the
outer core, at least, is believed to be liquid.

When an earthquake occurs waves are sent out through the
earth in all directions from the focus. Those waves which angle
down into the earth are bent or refracted back toward the surface
because the velocities of both the P and S waves increase with
depth in the mantle. Waves which are just tangent to the core are
refracted back and reach the surface approximately 103 degrees
from the epicenter. Those waves which strike the core at an angle
are bent into it because the speed is much less there than in the
neighboring mantle. These waves re-emerge from the core and

then after traversing the mantle on the other side reach the surface at least 143 degrees away from the epicenter. The core thus produces a "shadow zone" between 103 and 143 degrees away from the epicenter of any quake, where no direct P or S waves are received. Furthermore, beyond the shadow zone only the P waves

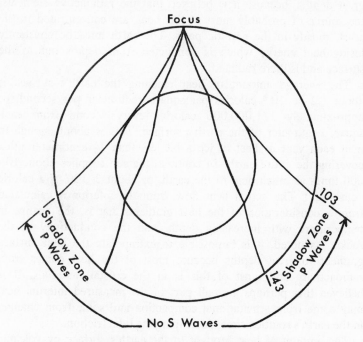

Seismic wave paths through the earth

are received, the liquid core acting like a filter to remove the shear-type waves. Surface waves, however, reach all parts of the earth. The action of the core in casting an earthquake shadow can be illustrated by assuming an epicenter at the north pole. In such a case both the P and S waves arrive at all points in the northern hemisphere, and as far south as 13 degrees south latitude (90 plus 13 equals 103). The shadow zone lies between 13 and 53 south latitude, and from 53 south to the south pole only the P waves arrive.

Evidence from deep mines and bore holes shows that everywhere the temperature of the crust increases with depth. The rate of increase varies greatly from place to place, with, however, a worldwide average of about 1 degree C for each 30 meters. In volcanic and hot spring areas the rate is understandably a great deal higher. The average rate is probably not maintained at very great depths, because it is believed that the radioactive elements, the source of probably most of this heat, are concentrated in the crust, mostly in the granitic parts. The earth must be constantly losing heat energy which is conducted from depths out to the surface and is there radiated.

The average amount of heat reaching the earth's surface is about 1.2×10^{-6} calories per square centimeter per second, or approximately 1/1,000,000 calories every second from each square centimeter of the earth's surface. This is about enough to melt each year a sheet of ice a bit less than ½ centimeter thick covering the entire earth. In contrast, the sun supplies about 10,-000 times as much heat to the earth, or about 3/100 of a calorie /cm²/sec.* The actual heat flow from the interior is calculated from a consideration of the heat gradient, that is, the change in temperature with increasing depth, and the conductivity of the rocks. As noted, it is impossible to extrapolate the near surface gradient to great depths because most of the heat comes from radioactivity and most of this is in the crustal materials. It is believed that perhaps a small part of the measured internal heat may come from gravitational compaction and some from changes in the earth's rotation time, accompanying tidal friction.

The amount of heat brought to the earth's surface by volcanic action and the amount of energy associated with earthquakes are both but a small fraction of the heat energy associated with the thermal gradient. A comparison of these three sources shows that the heat flow amounts to approximately 10^{28} ergs per year, the yearly earthquake energy to 10^{25} ergs, and the total volcanic heat energy 10^{26} ergs per year. Such a comparison indicates that thermal energy may be the ultimate source of energy which at times manifests itself in volcanic action and at other times in earthquakes.

---

* Calorie per square centimeter per second

Different types of rocks show a wide range in radioactivity. In some rare ore deposits more than ½ of a few cubic yards of ore may be uranium or thorium, whereas several cubic miles of very pure salt deposits may exhibit no measurable radioactivity. In general, the rate of production of radiogenic heat varies directly with the silica content of the rocks, that is, the granitelike rocks give the greatest amount of radioactive heat and the more basic simatic rocks, less. A crust 22 miles thick made entirely of granite should supply more heat than is actually escaping at the surface, even without allowance for original heat or for radioactive heat liberated in the underlying mantle or core. Thus other rocks than granite must be in the crust. The oceanic crust is composed largely of basalt, and one would expect a great deal less heat flow from it. However, the heat flow from the rocks in oceanic areas is much the same as from the continents. Thus in the ocean basins the heat must come from the upper part of the mantle, because the crust here lacks the granite type of rocks. This anomalous situation poses something of a problem, and the answer may lie in convection currents in the mantle, as we will see later. Since the total heat flow is far too small, the whole earth cannot be as highly radioactive as the crust. If it were, the flow of heat would of necessity be many times that observed. Radioactive elements thus must be largely concentrated in the uppermost layers of the earth.

Variations in the heat flow of the world show a close correlation with the global pattern of oceanic rises and ridges. The heat flow is greater than normal along the crest of these features, and low on the flanks.

The very extensive interconnecting mid-ocean ridge system runs for at least 40,000 miles across all the oceans and collectively covers an area equal to that of all the continents. After the continents and major ocean basins it comprises the third most important relief feature of the world. These ridges are both seismically and volcanically active, less so than the "Ring of Fire" around the Pacific, but they do mark the location of many shallow earthquakes and some volcanic activity. The ridge network, here and there, apparently extends into the continents as in the western part of the United States, and in Africa through the Rift Valley area. These rift valleys, such as that in which Lake Tanganyika lies, resemble very closely the ocean rifts. Tension rather than compression in the crust has been active in both. The worldwide mapping of the oceanic ridges has been greatly facilitated by their close genetic association with earthquakes. Earthquake epicenters have been mapped and then the ridges have been found to coincide in location.

The Mid-Atlantic Ridge is perhaps the best known of all. It was discovered in 1873 by the Challenger expedition in its epic 3½-year cruise around the world. It is an underwater ridge running north to south, about equally distant from the continents on either side. It joins the Indian Ocean ridges via an extension around Africa. There is a rift valley down the center which averages, for hundreds of miles, a depth of 6,000 feet and in many places is 8 to 30 miles wide. If exposed to view it would be a far more spectacular feature than the Grand Canyon of the Colorado River in Arizona, which is only about a mile deep at the maximum and approximately 13 miles wide.

Most of the Atlantic Ocean earthquakes have an epicenter in the Ridge zone, all at a relatively shallow depth, 30 kilometers at most. The rest of the ocean is seismically quiet. In total the Ridge is 1,000 to 1,200 miles wide including its summit and slopes. Note that the major deep earthquakes of the world, those up to 700 kilometers below the surface, are associated almost exclusively with the highly seismic areas around the Pacific Ocean.

The rocks comprising the Atlantic Ridge are primarily fine-grained vesicular basalts, with some serpentine and gabbro; it is thought that the latter have been brought up from the depths by faulting. Overlying the bedrock there is a thin coating of sediments. They lie on the flanks and top of the Ridge and cover and fill in low-lying pockets in the bedrock surface. In the northern part of the Ridge, at least, there is a very noticeable difference in age between very young volcanic rocks at the crest which show no weathering to older, more weathered, material on the flanks.

The East Pacific Rise is a vast low bulge on the sea floor, comparable in size with the Mid-Atlantic Ridge. Compared with the latter it is slightly less faulted at the crest. Like other oceanic ridges it marks the locus of shallow earthquakes, and has an abnormally high heat flow from the crestal areas. It is cross-cut by a number of faults and fracture zones. The major fractures do not seem to extend beyond the Rise, and are thus probably genetically associated with it. The topographic rise is matched by a downward bulge in the mantle-crust boundary. The Rise cuts across the Pacific from New Zealand to Mexico and thence into the Gulf of Lower California where the heat flow is three to four times higher than the world average.

According to some geologists, the East Pacific Rise continues under the western United States and goes to sea again in northern California. This suggestion has been made because the crust in the Basin and Range area is different from what hitherto has been considered normal continental structure.

Another major feature of the oceanic areas are arcuate groups of islands with their associated deep trenches. The island arcs of the West Pacific area are the best known and most typical, examples being the Aleutians, the Japanese Archipelago, and Indonesia. They lie on the continental side of the Andesite Line, are convex toward the central part of the Pacific Basin, and are bordered on their seaward side by oceanic deeps or trenches, generally over 25,000 feet deep. In some places there is a single line of islands and in others there is a double line. Volcanoes are associated with both single and double groups, but if they are double, as in the Sumatra and Java area, the volcanoes are on the inner arc, that is, on the side of the neighboring continent. Very deep focus earthquakes occur near the trench and the deeper the focus the nearer the continent will be their origin. Thus the earthquakes seem to emanate from a fracture zone which reaches the ocean floor on the side of the trenches and dips landward. In the Pacific Basin the motion along the fracture zones is such that the area as a whole seems to be slipping counterclockwise against the adjacent continents.

Island arcs appear in association with very marked gravity anomalies, both plus and minus. The large negative anomaly is centered on the trench slope toward the side of the arc, slightly away from the axis of the deepest part of the trench. This means that deep roots of crustal material must be present in these areas. The suggestion has been made that these low-density masses are kept down by the drag of a plunging mass of mantle material. Positive anomalies, that is, where the force of gravity is abnormally high, are centered on the islands of the arcs and must represent higher-density material there than normal.

The west coast of South America resembles in many respects the typical island arc of the West Pacific. Here, the zone of volcanoes, the Andes, does not form a group of islands but is part of the mainland. A deep trench lies off the coast and parallels it for a long distance, and a zone of earthquake foci intersects the surface somewhat offshore and descends eastward under the land, with increasing depth of origin. North America, outside of Alaska, lacks the island arc appearance. From Baja California to Alaska, the situation is atypical, the trench and the deep-to-intermediate-focus earthquake belt are missing, and the principal fault, the San Andreas, is here on the land.

The permanence of continents in their relationship one to another throughout geologic time is another major geologic problem and a review of some of the evidence both for and against the concept of continental drift will help to complete the over-all picture of earth structure.

In the southern hemisphere the Carboniferous to Lower Mesozoic history of Australia, India, Madagascar, South Africa, the Falkland Islands, South America and Antarctica are strikingly alike. In all of these places there is evidence of glaciation shown by the presence of consolidated till, or tillite, and glacial scratches, followed by a thick sequence of terrestrial deposits, both river and lake, with later on massive outpourings of basalt lava flows. Characteristically, there are coal deposits in the Upper Paleozoic layers. The type of life was distinctively alike in all places, and is exemplified by Glossopteris, a late Paleozoic fern, which occurs in all these areas, but was missing from the northern hemisphere.

Such a similarity of history has suggested to a number of geologists that these areas were at one time connected and perhaps formed a large land mass which has since been fragmented and the parts separated. The idea of continental drift, that is, that continents shift with respect to each other on some kind of a plastic layer, has thus been advocated because it explains otherwise inexplicable features.

The fact that Canada and Scandinavia since the retreat of the last glacier have risen on the average about one centimeter per year indicates certainly a plastic layer under the crust. And furthermore, the fact that isostatic equilibrium exists at all indicates that in response to various vertical forces the crust rises or sinks and such action must of necessity involve some concomitant flow of material under the crustal layers. Thus the idea of a sideways

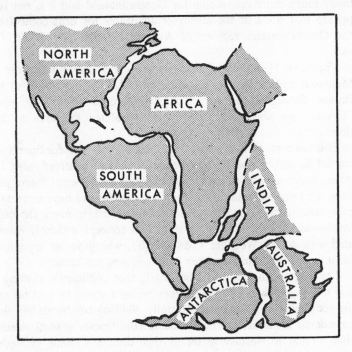

Continental drift may have separated the land areas from a late Paleozoic position similar to that illustrated.

shifting, or drifting over some plastic layer, if an adequate force is available, seems reasonable to many geologists.

If South America is moved in imagination over against Africa the coasts mesh remarkably closely, the Brazilian bulge fitting into the Gulf of Guinea. In fact, if the 6,500-foot depth contour is used as marking more truly the edge of the continents the fit is even closer. Other continents can be shifted in imagination, in various ways to see how they fit best together, and a number of geologists have had a hand at juggling continents in this fashion.

The first proposal was for one primeval continent called Pangaea, and later on it seemed best to assume two such early continents, one in the southern hemisphere, Gondwanaland, and one in the northern hemisphere, Laurasia. The evidence is certainly much more convincing for Gondwanaland and it is not surprising that some of the strongest advocates for drift come from the Gondwanaland regions of Australia, India, and South Africa.

The term "Gondwana" was given to the Upper Paleozoic to Mesozoic group of rocks in India, in 1872, by a geologist of the Indian Geological Survey. The name comes from the name "Gonds," an aboriginal tribe which inhabited the area at one time.

The concept of continental drift states that the continents all started as either one or two primeval masses centered near the poles, and that they started to break apart under some force, perhaps tidal or rotational, in the early Mesozoic and have continued ever since to move on a weak suboceanic crust, in much the same fashion as ice drifts through water. This concept is closely associated with Alfred Wegener (1880-1930), who gave his arguments for it in 1912, and in a number of subsequent publications.

The suggestion has also been made that continental drifting is due to changes in centrifugal forces brought about by erosion and the redistribution of material laterally. Shifting continents are thus considered a manifestation of lateral adjustments toward equilibrium similar to isostasy in the vertical direction. Some geologists call on the low-velocity, plastic layer in the upper mantle to be the zone in which slippage may primarily occur.

For a time the concept of drifting continents was in eclipse, but more recently it has been resurrected to explain some very interesting data concerning paleomagnetism. The magnetic pole of the past, and thus presumably the pole of rotation, has shifted its position very markedly as indicated by the remnant magnetism of magnetite and related minerals in lavas and sandstones. The idea here is that magnetic mineral fragments line themselves up with the prevailing magnetic field of the earth as they settle into a sediment or freeze out of a lava, and will from then on maintain this early orientation regardless of what happens to the continent on which they lie. Paleomagnetic evidence for continental drift is striking. The pole positions as measured by rock specimens have shifted widely from those of today, and moreover, the pole position for each of the continents has differed from that of the others, not coinciding at the same time in geologic history. Thus a shifting of one continent with respect to another is a reasonable explanation. In Australia the paleomagnetically determined latitude abruptly increased by more than 50 degrees between Devonian and Carboniferous times, while coral reefs disappeared and glaciation began. This, of course, suggests a marked shift of Australia with respect to the poles.

Paleowind directions as given by the shapes of fossilized sand dunes and by cross-bedding seem to be in rough accord with the changed Paleomagnetic pole positions of the past. Furthermore, glacial deposits have been found in the equatorial areas and coral reefs in polar regions, seeming to indicate that the climate anyway was different in the past in these areas, and perhaps that the continental areas have changed position with respect to the poles.

Evidence concerning the temperature of the oceans of the past is given by a consideration of the ratio of two oxygen isotopes, O^{18}/O^{16}. The oxygen in the calcium carbonate shells of marine organisms shows a change in this ratio accompanying a change in the temperature of precipitation. Data using this method seems to indicate rather marked changes of temperature in the past, but what they may mean with respect to possible shifts of pole position is perhaps another matter.

The evidence for drift is lengthy and includes a number of other items, and collectively is conclusive for many geologists. However, for many others the evidence against continental drift is equally strong. It has been argued that the fit of various continental masses may be fortuitous. Furthermore, the question is asked, Why did the drifting start suddenly when it did? and there is some feeling that there is no adequate known force available to move continents over the presumed underlying plastic layer. Similarity of faunas and floras, in now widely separated regions, can often be explained by former land bridges, that is, land connections which have now been flooded by the sea. Furthermore, animals and plants have both been found to be adept at traveling very long distances. Winds can blow seeds for many miles across the oceans and fairly large animals can be rafted on driftwood.

The diversity and range of the marine one-celled animals, the Foraminifera, show a close correlation with temperature as determined by latitude, and thus locate the present pole of rotation. Similar analyses of the life of the past such as some Permian Brachiopods show a pole near its present position and a study of the range and distribution of the Eocene flora shows a climatic control, again centered about the present pole positions. Thus, such studies seem to demonstrate the permanence of the various continents with respect to the poles, at least from the Permian on to the present.

The localization of deep earthquakes down to 720 kilometers at the ocean-continent boundaries, especially around the Pacific, demonstrates the very deep structure of the continents, and such a deep structure must place relatively heavy restrictions on any theory of continental drift. It means to many geologists, that the drifting masses must be much thicker than had previously been suggested.

The question of continental drift is still very much an open one. There is strong evidence on each side.

CHAPTER XVII

ORIGIN OF MOUNTAINS
AND EARLY HISTORY OF
THE EARTH

Diastrophism and igneous activity are both undoubtedly powered by heat energy coming from the interior of the earth. A major problem for the geologist concerns the kind of mechanism which turns heat energy into that needed for twisting, pushing, and uplifting of large segments of the crust. Is this due to convection currents in the mantle, to expansion and contraction of rocks resulting from changes in atomic arrangement, or does the explanation lie in some other process?

Mountain-building has many different aspects which need to be considered in any coherent explanation. In the first place, why do geosynclines occur, and why after a certain depth of sedimentation or perhaps lapse of time is there folding, uplift, and thrust-faulting? Why after folding are such areas characteristically uplifted and eroded, perhaps a number of times? How can the obvious genetic association of volcanoes, island arcs, and deep-sea trenches be explained, as well as the general picture of the oceanic ridges and rises and the heat-flow data of the world as a whole?

In 1890 G. K. Gilbert in his classic monograph on Lake Bonneville, the precursor and much larger edition of the present Great

Salt Lake of Utah, described broad swelling movements of the land as necessary to explain the present topography, and called them epeirogenetic, distinguishing them from orogenic, or mountain-building movements. Since then such differential continental warping has been accepted as very widespread, and the acknowledgment of its importance has been helped by the concept of isostasy and by a recognition of the very marked changes in elevation of Scandinavia and northern Canada following the disappearance of ice from those areas. The belief now is that the crust is quite weak and shifts readily in response to applied forces. It has been suggested that under the crust in the upper mantle the strength of many rocks is actually very small and some plastic flow might occur at stress levels of a very low magnitude.

In recognition of such weakness and the rapidity with which isostatic equilibrium is attained it becomes a little difficult to explain why many mountain areas seem to have been eroded to a relatively flat surface, after which upwarping took place with renewed erosion. The question arises as to why the crust remained stationary long enough for the peneplain to develop, probably a matter of some millions of years.

Faulting and folding in the crust could well be the result of some kind of differential motion of material in the mantle, which is reflected in the crust by its attempt to conform to the underlying mantle changes. Motion in the mantle, due to convection currents, is one suggested mechanism.

Convection currents can explain a multitude of observations: ocean ridges, fold mountains, major faulting, drifting continents, and the heat-flow pattern of the world. The general idea is that mantle material is heated more in one place than in another. The hot material expands, thus becomes less dense and rises at one place to sink elsewhere. The mantle rises under oceanic ridges and falls under the oceanic deep-sea trenches and fold mountain areas, with a postulated rate of flow of a very few centimeters per year. The extensive network of ocean ridges, which show tension cracks and volcanic activity, certainly suggests an upward push by hot liquid from underneath. Such a picture is also consistent with the high heat flow along the ridges which is much greater than average. Some of the greatest gravity deficiencies ever recorded have been found along the trenches as well as much less than average heat. The trenches perhaps mark the places of crustal compression where convection currents carry the cool, less dense sialic material downward with an active flow. It has been suggested that geosynclines and trenches are similar in origin and that trenches are not filled with sediments because they are too far

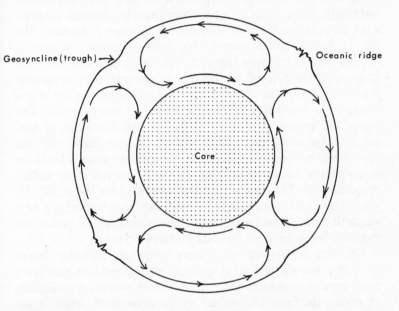

Convection currents in the mantle may explain the origin of oceanic ridges and geosynclines.

away from an adequate source, and further, that perhaps the continents grow by the accumulation of the lighter "foam" of the mantle material before the major part sinks under the continental mass.

The rate of flow of material during convection has been estimated in a number of ways. For instance, the rate of uplift of glaciated lands gives a means of calculating the speed of mantle readjustments. The proper order of magnitude is apparently about one centimeter per year. A similar rate has also been estimated by assuming that the faulting along the western margin of the Americas is due to the shifting of this part of the crust with respect to the Pacific Basin. The rate of shift has been determined from an analysis of the amount of seismic energy which is released on the average along this zone. Such estimates are of course only approximations and depend a great deal on reasonable values for relatively unknown quantities. Incidentally, the mere existence of such seismically active faults along the west margin of North America must be evidence for shift with respect to other continents. The rate of flow of crustal material has been determined recently in another way. It has been shown that the volcanic rocks of the sea floor on either side of the oceanic ridges and rises apparently becomes older as the distance from the volcanically active ridges increases. It seems that new material emerges along the rises and ridges and spreads away from them. The calculated rate of such sea-floor spreading varies from one to between three and four centimeters per year. The dating of the volcanic rocks is based on a recognition that there has been a periodic reversal of the earth's magnetic field. The present polarity has existed for about 700,000 years. Once such a reversal chronology has been worked out by a magnetic study of the rocks, and key dates obtained by radioactive methods, it can obviously be used for further dating.

The idea of convection currents forms an attractive theory because it ties together many geologic phenomena and provides a force capable of deforming the earth's crust, without the necessity of having the force transmitted by the crust itself, which is too weak for this purpose. It explains why tension and compression of the crust can occur at the same time, hard to explain by either pure contraction or expansion of the earth. The compression zones are the island arcs and fold mountains, and the tension zones the mid-ocean ridges and rift valleys.

Force is applied to the crust by the frictional drag of the moving mass of mantle material. The mantle in this action has been likened to a thick stew churning in a pot and the continents to areas of thick scum moving on the surface. Local horizontal shear can be introduced by horizontal gradients of temperature in the mantle, and one presumably should get strike-slip faulting as a result. Incidentally, if convection currents involve the whole mantle, as many believe, the chemical composition of the mantle should tend to be more or less uniform throughout.

Wegener's primeval continent Pangaea was perhaps swept together as flotsam on the mantle by the action of convection and later, because of the insulating action of this proto-continent the direction of convection reversed itself, and thus destroyed what it had initially formed. Some geologists postulate five convection cells in each hemisphere and many believe that this number was once less, but has increased as the thickness of the mantle decreased due to the loss of iron to the core.

The shape of the geoid, that is, the shape of the water surface of the world has been obtained recently in much more detail than was previously possible, by using data from artificial satellites. The path of these bodies is not perfectly smooth but changes up and down by a few hundred feet as they pass over the low- to high-gravity areas of the earth. Such anomalies in gravity show up as bulges and depressions in the geoid, of at most a few hundred feet. For example, in part of the Indian Ocean the water level is somewhat over 100 feet lower because the gravity is relatively so weak there that the seawater is not drawn together to the depth expectable if the whole earth were subject to uniform gravitational forces, and in the nearby Indonesian area the geoid has a bulge of about 100 feet, because of a relatively greater gravitational attraction. Such anomalies of the geoid seem to be correlated with heat-flow observations, depressions with relatively high heat flow and bulges with relatively low. Such a relationship can be explained by an upward-moving convection mass in the mantle having less density and a higher temperature than normal, and a downdraft of the mantle having a higher density and a lower temperature.

A group of suggestions for the origin of mountains is based on the concept that a decrease of the volume of material under the crust will result in a wrinkling of the crust so as to conform to new and shorter distances. Of historic interest was the early suggestion that the earth contracted on cooling from an initially much hotter condition. This theory, as we have seen, had to be discarded when the process of radioactivity was discovered. Other more plausible suggestions call for the formation of an assemblage of denser minerals at depth from a group of less dense ones by a rearrangement of atoms, or by the extrusion of lava, both of which would lead to local diminution of mantle volume and the wrinkling of the crust above it.

In opposition to this idea, the suggestion has been made that parts of the mantle have expanded. In order to produce expansion all that is needed is to change solid rock into magma, or to form an assemblage of less dense minerals from a group of denser ones. For example, the changing of olivine into serpentine by the addition of water results in an increase in volume. If the expansion is localized, large-scale welts are formed, down the sides of which material could move to give a folded and faulted mass at the bottom.

Such gravitational sliding, considered by many geologists to be one of the very important explanations for many deformed mountain features, requires first that a large segment of the crust be uplifted by some means, then gravity causes the flowing or creeping of the uplifted mass downhill, under its own weight. Gravity-sliding tectonics demonstrate, of course, that epeirogenetic movements, that is, bulging of the crust in one place, can result in orogenically deformed material. An excellent example of this type of deformation has been described in the northern Apennines of Italy. Here, a mass of rock more than four by seven kilometers is apparently separated from its source. Most of the competent beds, the layers which should transmit forces, are not in contact with one another in this area. They form a train of isolated blocks, incapable of transmitting a push. The suggestion here has been made that before elevation of the area above sea level, a welt developed on the sea floor, and that materials slid down the sides of this. Then the whole area was uplifted and eroded and we have what we see today.

Suggestions for the ultimate origin of mountains are highly conjectural, based as they are in varying degrees on laboratory experiments which attempt to recreate times and conditions prevailing in the earth. In the last few decades, however, a number of developments have greatly helped in basic understanding. The mechanical properties of various rocks under very high temperatures and pressures have been investigated in the laboratory and much has been found out about their probable behavior within the earth. Furthermore, a great deal has been learned about the ocean areas of the earth with respect to structures and types of rock, and thus a more coordinated worldwide picture is emerging.

It may be that a number of the mountain-building mechanisms are effective, that both expansion and contraction have been active and that no one explanation will fit all the observations. Part of the story seems to be clear in certain cases; for instance, in some it seems to be true that gravity-sliding is the answer. But this is only part of the picture, because the mechanism which has caused the initial bulge in the earth is still unclear. And the mechanism associated with the whole geosynclinal cycle of downwarping, sedimentation, folding, and subsequent times of uplift is still an enigma.

Many theories have been proposed regarding the origin of the earth and its early history. All must of course take into account the most noticeable peculiarity of the solar system, that is, the regularity of motions of the planets and their satellites. Such a regularity strongly suggests a common origin for the system as a whole. The planets all revolve around the sun in the same direction, counterclockwise as viewed from above the north pole of the earth, in nearly circular orbits, and in more or less the same plane. Furthermore, the sun, and as far as is known all the planets rotate in the same counterclockwise direction, except for Uranus, whose axis of rotation lies almost in its orbital plane. The satellite systems of the planets closely resemble the planetary system, with motions in the same directions except for a few outer satellites.

Earth-origin theories can be divided into two groups. One assumes an interaction between the sun and another star as causing some kind of catastrophic change and the development of the planets at some time after the sun was formed. The second group of theories assumes the slow evolution of a primordial system, with the formation of the sun and planets at about the same time. Theories involving the catastrophic close approach of another star or actual collision, such as the Chamberlin-Moulton Planetesimal Hypothesis or the Jeans-Jeffreys Tidal Theory have been largely abandoned by astronomers, and an explanation at the present time is being sought in the evolution of an extended system initially containing gas and solid particles.

Historically, the Nebular Hypothesis of Kant and Laplace, developed in the early years of the nineteenth century, is the most important of the second group. This theory assumed an initial slowly rotating sperical cloud of hot gases. As gravitational contraction occurred the rotation rate speeded up, and the whole mass flattened into a disk. The increase in rotational rate with the decrease in size was inevitable if angular momentum were to be preserved. Rings of material, which later collected into planets, were left behind when the centrifugal force of the outer material equaled the inward gravitational pull. This theory was abandoned for a number of reasons, chief among which perhaps was the observation that the planets with less than 1 per cent of the mass of the solar system as a whole collectively possessed 98 per cent of the angular momentum, and if the sun had been rotating fast enough to drop off a ring where Mercury now revolves it should be rotating more than a hundred times as rapidly as it now is.

The older ideas of an initially gaseous, then wholly molten, earth have now changed to a generally accepted origin wherein there was an accretion of low-temperature particles with a later segregation of material into core, mantle, and crust. It seems impossible that the ocean was ever present as a vapor over the earth, and the surface rocks molten at the same time, because at melted rock temperatures, that is, approximately 1200 degrees C, the water vapor would have extended 12,000 kilometers up, and the upper molecules would be far enough away from the earth with a large enough velocity to escape from the earth's gravitational field. The water molecules in the upper atmosphere in addition would probably be dissociated into hydrogen and oxygen by solar radiation and particle bombardment and as such, being smaller and lighter, would escape still faster.

The group of current hypotheses of solar origin assume that stars may be forming continuously from slowly rotating clouds of cold dust and gas. Such masses heat up under gravitational self-compression until the center becomes hot enough to initiate nuclear reactions. The nuclear furnace is thus kindled, and a bright glowing star is formed. If, in the course of contraction the rotation rate is proper, masses of loosely aggregated material will be left behind, which in their own turn may on further contraction leave material which eventually forms satellites. The planets in course of time will also heat up by the kinetic energy of infalling particles, compression, tidal friction, and most important of all by radioactivity. With such a suggested origin for the solar system, it is believed by many that the formation of other planetary systems may be a fairly common event in the universe.

The inability of the Nebular Hypothesis to explain the present slow rotation rate of the sun may be overcome by assuming a magnetic type of braking according to some astronomers. If the sun initially rotated very rapidly and had a stronger magnetic field than it does at present the ejection of charged particles through this field, which of course rotated with the sun, would cause the transfer of angular momentum from the sun to the charged particles. In such a fashion the sun would lose angular momentum and thus slow down in its rotation rate, and the ejected particles would be speeded up and gain momentum, before they finally passed beyond the effective reach of the solar magnetic field.

The suggested origin of the earth starts with the accretion of material whose composition resembled that of a mixture of stony and metallic meteorites, to form an unsorted kind of conglomeratic earth. This occurred over 5 billion years ago. The separation of the mantle and core is most easily explained by the melting at one time or another of the greater part of the earth, allowing the descent of the iron and nickel and other metals to form the core, and the ascent of the lighter materials, the silicates, to form the mantle.

In the early days of the earth the rate of radioactive heat production was probably a number of times greater than at the present, because there was a great deal more radioactive material. Specifically, radioactive potassium which has a half-life of about ¼ the age of the earth would have been present in a much greater percentage than today. Possibly the early earth thermally expanded as a result of radioactive heat and cracks developed in the cold outer layer. It has been suggested that crustal material, richer in radioactive elements, oozed out of these cracks. The continents may have been largely formed from this material fairly early in earth history, with perhaps the continued slow growth throughout geologic time by the addition of material from the mantle.

As we have seen, the study of isotopes has had a far-reaching effect on the methods of geochronology. Now in the investigation of the crust and mantle it comes to the aid of the geologist again. The ratio of rubidium to strontium, Rb/Sr, is, on the average, larger in crustal rocks than in mantle material. As a result of the decay of the radioactive form of rubidium, Rb^{87}, its daughter strontium Sr^{87} is generally more abundant in relation to nonradiogenic strontium in the crust than in the mantle. Thus rocks and minerals which have been involved in crustal processes may often be distinguished from those which have come directly from the mantle. Furthermore, a consideration of the ratio Rb/Sr can be used to determine the age of crustal material and the time at which it may have been derived from the mantle. Such considerations have led some geologists to the conclusion that the continents have continued to grow by the addition of mantle material.

Any discussion of the early history of the earth must take into account the over-all effects of gravitation of the earth and moon one on the other, and especially the changes in rotation due to tidal friction. The mutual tidal action of two bodies rotating about each other varies inversely as the square of the distance between them. If a satellite is within less than 2.44 times the radius of the planet and if the densities are the same, the tidal effects on the satellite are so great that it will break into small particles. Such an occurrence may have taken place, according to some geologists, between the moon and the earth, and some of the initial moon material may have been captured by the earth to form the continents, and the rest of it reassembled to produce the moon as we know it. Since then, tidal friction has slowed up the rotation time of the earth and the distance between the earth and the moon has increased. Incidentally, with the moon closer to the earth the ocean tides would have been much higher, and with the rotation time less they would have swept around the earth more frequently than they do now.

Independent evidence for the slowing up of the earth's rotation is given by certain ridges in the skeleton structure of corals which may be due to a daily growth cycle. Recent corals show 360 such ridges per year, while Devonian corals show 400 per year. The rate of rotation change calculated from such data correlates with that from tidal friction, and equals about 1.8 thousands of a second per century.

The earth's atmosphere and the oceans have probably both been derived by the de-gassing of mantle material. Volcanic activity probably supplied the waters of the world which have been added throughout geologic time, and the salts in the sea came primarily from the weathering of the crustal rocks. The early atmosphere of the earth was perhaps composed of methane, ammonia, and water vapor, which had been in the frozen state as the earth initially formed, or perhaps were retained chemically until the earth was large enough with an adequate gravitational field to hold them in gaseous form. The formation of a plentiful oxygen atmosphere waited until the activity of plant life. Such life has been identified in Precambrian rocks almost 2 billion years old, and thus oxygen, at least locally around centers of growing organisms, must have been present at that time. By 1.2 billion years ago enough oxygen was present so that extensive beds of sandstone, stained red by iron oxide, could be formed.

The deposition of sandstone early in earth history implies of course the activity of weathering and erosion as well as the presence of quartz-bearing rock, that is, a sialic crust.

The location and size of early land areas is conjectural. It is really not known whether the major ocean basins are ancient or relatively recent, whether the continental crust was formed early in earth history and the present continents are merely reworked material, whether they are continually being increased by material from the upper mantle, or perhaps were created by the infall of low-density lunar or meteoric substance. Paleomagnetic evidence for shifting poles is controversial, as are continental drift and convection currents. It should be emphasized again that it is extremely difficult to extrapolate from the results obtained in laboratory experiments on various types of rocks with the necessarily short laboratory time scale, to the time scales which must be assumed for geological actions. The geotectonic synthesis of all structural geology is one of the most fascinating, but certainly the most unsatisfactory, phases of geology at the present time. Many concepts have been advanced, based, on the whole, on rather flimsy evidence.

We find that the geomorphology of the surface of the earth, the explanation of scenery in terms of weathering and erosion, is relatively clear. We must accept, however, the heterogeneous occurrence of rocks and mountains and volcanic zones. In other words, geology has done an excellent job of reconstructing with great success the events which have produced the modern scene, but it has been up to now far less successful in discovering the basic causes which have produced the major crustal features of the earth.

FURTHER READING

LANDFORMS AND THEIR ORIGIN

Leet, L. D., and Judson, Sheldon. *Physical Geology* (3rd ed.; Englewood Cliffs: Prentice-Hall, 1965) An excellent college level textbook.

Lobeck, A. K. *Things Maps Don't Tell Us* (New York: Macmillan, 1956).
A stimulating discussion of how shapes shown on maps can tell a great deal about the kind of rocks, structure, and geologic history of an area.

Mather, K. F. *The Earth Beneath Us* (New York: Random House, 1964).
A superbly illustrated book on the making of landscapes.

Nace, R. L. "Water Management, Agriculture, and Groundwater Supplies." *U. S. Geol. Surv. Circular 415*, 1960.

Shelton, John S. *Geology Illustrated* (San Francisco: Freeman, 1966).
A marvelous sequence of pictures which illustrate rocks and earth processes is accompanied by a lucid and provocative text.

Shimer, John A. *This Scupltured Earth* (New York: Columbia University Press, 1959).
A discussion of the origin of the various landscape features of the United States. For the interested layman.

Thornbury, W. D. *Regional Geomorphology of the United States* (New York: John Wiley, 1965).
A systematic discussion of each physiographic province of the United States. Well illustrated.

Wyckoff, Jerome. *Rock, Time, and Landforms* (New York: Harper & Row, 1966).
An excellent account of the reasons for the changing landscapes of the world. Copiously illustrated with examples primarily from North America and Europe.

MEN AND IDEAS; HISTORY OF GEOLOGY

Adams, F. D. *The Birth and Development of the Geological Sciences* (New York: Dover, 1938).

A systematic, interesting account of changing ideas concerning various aspects of the earth from ancient times into the nineteenth century.

Fenton, C. L., and Fenton, M. A. *Giants of Geology* (Garden City: Doubleday, 1952).

A popular account of some of the pioneer geologists.

Geikie, A. *The Founders of Geology* New York: Dover, 1962).

A reprint of a book first published by Macmillan in 1897. An excellent discussion of the development of geology and the men involved, from the Greeks to the end of the nineteenth century.

GEOCHRONOLOGY

Faul, H. *Ages of Rock, Planets and Stars* (New York: McGraw-Hill, 1966).

An excellent, up-to-date summary of radioactive methods of dating.

Hurley, P. M. *How Old is the Earth* (Garden City: Doubleday Anchor Book, 1959).

A fine book for the general reader. It gives a good introduction to the various methods used for dating geological events and materials.

Kulp, J. Laurence. "Geologic Time Scale," *Science,* Vol. 133, 14 April 1961, pp. 1105-1114.

IGNEOUS ACTIVITY

Bullard, F. M. *Volcanoes* (Austin: University of Texas Press, 1962).

A very readable discussion of all aspects of volcanic activity.

Williams, Howel. *Crater Lake, the Story of Its Origin* (Berkeley: University of California Press, 1954).

A clear, well-illustrated discussion of the origin of this scenic attraction. Written for the layman.

GLACIERS

Dyson, J. L. *The World of Ice* (New York: Knopf, 1962).

A dramatic presentation of the development, extent and landscape-producing activities of glaciers.

Flint, R. F. *Glacial and Pleistocene Geology* (New York: John Wiley, 1957).

An account of glacial phenomena and deposits by an expert in the field.

Matthes, F. E. *The Incomparable Valley* ed. F. Fryxell, (Berkeley: University of California Press, 1950).

A beautiful job of telling the geologic story of Yosemite Valley.

MAJOR EARTH STRUCTURES: CRUST, MANTLE, AND CORE

Barth, T. F. W. *Theoretical Petrology* (2nd ed.; New York: John Wiley, 1962).

Heezen, B. C. "The Rift in the Ocean Floor," *Scientific American,* Vol. 203, October, 1960, pp. 98-110.

Howell, B, F., Jr. *Introduction to Geophysics* (New York: McGraw-Hill, 1959).
A college textbook. Includes discussions on geomagnetism, causes of mountain-building, tectonic patterns of the world, and a great deal about earthquakes, their origin, transmission, and what they tell about the earth.

Jacobs, J. A., Russell, R. D., and Wilson, J. T. *Physics and Geology* (New York: McGraw-Hill, 1959).
A wide-ranging advanced-level discussion of many aspects of earth structure and composition, from the center to the surface.

Menard, H. W. *Marine Geology of the Pacific* (New York: McGraw-Hill, 1964).
A lucid discussion of the major geological structures of the Pacific region and their probable origin, by an expert. Includes trenches, island arcs, oceanic rises, submarine canyons, turbidity currents, shelfs, and slopes.

Takahashi, T., and Bassett, W. A. "The Composition of the Earth's Interior," *Scientific American,* June, 1965.
A discussion of techniques for testing materials under high pressures and some thoughts on the composition of the earth's core.

Wilson, J. T. "Continental Drift" *Scientific American,* April, 1963.
A well-illustrated, very readable article. Includes a brief history of the idea of drifting continents.

HISTORY OF THE EARTH

Clark, T. H., and Stearn, C. W. *The Geological Evolution of North America* (New York: Ronald Press, 1960).
The geologic history of North America from a regional standpoint. A college text.

Kay, M., and Colbert, E. H. *Stratigraphy and Life History* (New York: John Wiley, 1964).
An advanced, detailed discussion of earth history. Well illustrated. Includes much about geosynclines, continental drift, and a chapter on the origin of the earth.

INDEX